"But you didn't want to be a rich and famous model,"

Race said with deep understanding. "You wanted to paint."

"I don't think I can—now," Andrea said. "I've wasted too much time on other things."

Race was looking at her strangely, his dark eyes glowing and intense. "It's very easy, really," he said softly, taking her hand in his and playing with her fingers. "All you have to do is make a commitment with your heart." For an instant she caught her breath as he stared deeply into her eyes. "I'll show you how."

Dear Reader:

We at Silhouette are very excited to bring you this reading **Sensation**. *Look out for the four books which appear in our Silhouette* **Sensation** *series every month. These stories will have the high quality you have come to expect from Silhouette, and their varied and provocative plots will encourage you to explore the wonder of falling in love – again and again!*

Emotions run high in these drama-filled novels. Greater sensual detail and an extra edge of realism intensify the hero and heroine's relationship so that you cannot help but be caught up in their every change of mood.

We hope you enjoy this **Sensation** *– and will go on to enjoy many more.*

We would love to hear your comments and encourage you to write to us:

Jane Nicholls
Silhouette Books
PO Box 236
Thornton Road
Croydon
Surrey
CR9 3RU

ANN MAJOR
Seize the Moment

Silhouette Sensation

First published in Great Britain in 1993
by Silhouette Books, Eton House, 18-24 Paradise Road,
Richmond, Surrey TW9 1SR

© Ann Major 1984

Silhouette, Silhouette Sensation and Colophon are
Trade Marks of Harlequin Enterprises B.V.

ISBN 0 373 59032 6

18-9311

Made and printed in Great Britain

Other novels by Ann Major

Silhouette Desire

Dream Come True
Meant To Be
Love Me Again
The Wrong Man
Golden Man
Beyond Love
In Every Stranger's Face
What This Passion Means
* Passion's Child
* Destiny's Child
* Night Child
* Wilderness Child
* Scandal's Child
* The Goodbye Child
A Knight in Tarnished Armor
Married to the Enemy

* *Children of Destiny Series*

Silhouette Special Edition

Brand of Diamonds
Dazzle
The Fairy Tale Girl

Silhouette Christmas Stories 1992
"Santa's Special Miracle"

Silhouette Summer Sizzlers 1993
"The Barefooted Enchantress"

This book is dedicated to Sondra Stanford,
a fellow creative spirit,
who has added immeasurably to my life.

She's encouraged me in dark moments,
laughed with me in bright ones,
traveled with me to far places
that would have been lonely
without her companionship.

Thank you, Sondra, for being there.

Chapter 1

THE LATE-EVENING SUMMER HEAT FROM THE THICK YUCA-
tan jungle rose up the narrow limestone steps of the
ancient Mayan temple, smothering every living creature with its suffocating presence—everyone except
Andrea Ford. She suddenly went cold, as though it
were an Arctic wind gusting up those steps.

She was electric with fear, frozen for an instant—
statue still—as coolly immobile as the stone columns
around her, as terrified as an Indian maiden who'd
mounted the temple to be sacrificed centuries ago.

Andrea's body heat seemed to flow out of her in a
rush, and her teeth felt ridiculously like they might start
chattering if she didn't hastily clamp them together.
Goosebumps prickled over every inch of her long, lithe
body.

Despite the steaming intensity of the heat, she
shuddered violently, feeling as she always did when
such an attack was upon her, a terrified fool. She

almost welcomed the flamboyant Fendi fur coat she was modeling, as she snuggled more deeply beneath the thickness of its elaborate folds and sank back in a seemingly negligent pose against the fierce stone idol, Chac-Mool.

Her air of relaxation poorly masked her inner turbulence. Two deep, hastily drawn breaths did little to calm her.

There was nothing to be afraid of—not here—she attempted to reassure herself.

Several steps below her, and surrounded by mountains of cameras, Stefano was perched precariously on the temple's steep stairs, his familiar dark head bent over his favorite Nikon as he reloaded and changed lenses. She knew better than to call down to him for reassurance, for his every savage gesticulation and his incessant mumblings in his native Italian, all so familiar to her, told her how acute was his frustration with his equipment. He was losing the precious golden light as the shadows in the jungle deepened.

The other models were milling at the base of the temple, giggling amongst themselves, smoking, and drinking soft drinks a Mexican vendor had cajoled them into buying. In that moment Andrea longed to be down there with them, to be one of them, to forget her terror in the exchange of model-talk about difficulties with powerful agents, egotistical photographers, and hairdos—trivial chatter she usually found tedious.

Again she drew a deep breath. But the fear did not go away as quickly as it had seized Andrea. It never did. As always it drained away very slowly. This very fear, these little nervous attacks—she called them— were the reason she had fled New York precisely when she most needed to be working.

When she'd informed her agent, Luci Stevens, that she had agreed to shoot a poorly paid fashion magazine editorial assignment in Mexico and afterwards planned to take off three weeks to rest, Luci had erupted like a human volcano, tearing her over-large glasses from her lined face and swinging them wildly around as she ranted that Andrea was getting older and would soon find herself a nobody again, her name ripped from the agency's headsheet and her billings suffering from such irresponsible behavior. Luci was in the middle of accusing her star model of going only to enjoy the ruins, an indulgence she thought Andrea gave in to all too frequently, reminding Andrea, and very heatedly, that in the last six months Andrea had been to Rome, Greece, Pompeii, and Egypt on similar assignments.

Andrea's mischievous, velvet-soft purr interrupted her agent in mid-tirade. "Aren't you forgetting Borobudur, Luci?"

"Good grief! I can't even pronounce that wretched God-forsaken place."

"Bo-ro—"

"Do you think I care how you say it!" Luci screeched theatrically. "What you get out of constantly running off to these far-flung, impoverished, not to mention horribly uncomfortable. . . ."

"Perhaps, Luci," Andrea began, her normally gentle voice hardening, "you should remember that despite my great age, and admittedly 32 is ancient for a model, you still need me—more than I need you. If I can't take off when I desperately need to get away . . ."

Whatever Luci's real feelings were, she instantly concealed them, her attitude changing visibly, at least superficially. Her tone became so placating that Andrea almost wondered if she'd imagined the hysterics of a moment before. "Whatever you want or need, Andy dear. You're the boss. . . . But do call me . . . when you get back in town."

Andrea had confided in no one, not even Luci, her real reasons for leaving New York—that she was a bundle of nerves. She had hoped that Don would call before she left so she could have at least told him that she would be flying down to Mexico to join him. All her calls had been answered by that maddening recording of his. She'd even gone to the lavish co-op on Park Avenue overlooking the park, where he stayed when he was in town, and left a note with one of the doormen; but all her efforts to contact him had failed. Thus, tonight, she would be forced to surprise him at the airport or his rented villa if she were to see him, and she hated doing that. But she simply had to be with him, she had to tell him what was happening to her. He was the only person she felt close to.

Andrea Ford, "Andy" only to her closest friends and associates, was a glorious, superstar model, one of those glamorous figments of the fashion world's Never Never Land, and the only authentic superstar on Luci's headsheet. From one exclusive cosmetic contract Andy earned for a month's work each year what it took most executives to earn in five. But, as Luci pointed out with increasing frequency, the days of a model's lucrative career were numbered. Fortunately Andy had prepared for the unhappy day when she was too old to model. She'd invested heavily in real estate, initially as a means of sheltering her income. Then she'd grown genuinely interested in making money.

Over the years Andy had dabbled successfully in stocks as well, while she continued to invest heavily in real estate. If she was independent, it was only because she could afford to be.

Andrea lay against the warm stone idol, the wild hammering of her heart scarcely lessening. Its beats seemed to be the only sound in the vast silence. She hated herself when she was nervous like this, and struggled to get a grip on her emotions. Surely here in Mexico—thousands of miles from New York City—she was safe. She had to be!

Three months ago fear had been an emotion unknown to her. Then the inexplicable late night phone calls had begun, those terrifyingly threatening calls that had made her brow bead with perspiration even on the coldest of nights, as she lay in her bed alone trying to sleep so that she would look fresh for her next morning's assignments. She'd had her number changed to an unlisted one, but that hadn't helped for long. The police had traced several of the calls, always to a coin telephone in a different section of the city. More than once of late a photographer had advised her to get to bed earlier, not knowing the real reason she'd had to apply makeup more thickly to conceal the gray shadows beneath her famous green eyes.

Suddenly the phone calls had ceased as abruptly as they had begun, and she'd been lulled into feeling that whoever had been calling had lost interest in her. Then last Tuesday, after drinks at the Plaza with friends, a car had careened out of nowhere and almost run her down. Even when she'd staggered breathlessly backward against the curb as though hit, the black Buick had blitzed past her, weaving in and out between cars, its tires squealing, disappearing into the shadows of Central Park, never looking back. She'd known then that the accident had been no accident, but a deliberate attempt to run her down, and this knowledge had shaken her deeply.

She had an enemy. And she didn't know who or why.

Of course, when one climbed as high and as fast as she had, when one stayed at the top year after year defying all the odds, one made enemies. But not the kind that ran one down at street corners. There were other models who resented her strange, backdoor ascent up the ladder to fame and fortune, other girls who played by the rules, and didn't like it when an outsider climbed to the top without even knowing the first thing about the game. They couldn't know that her success meant little more than a means of paying her bills, that she'd failed miserably in the two pursuits that mattered most to her—her marriage and her painting.

Andrea moved away from the idol, toward the edge of the Temple of the Warriors and looked down, shading her eyes and trying not to squint lest she mar her makeup. What was it that had brought her fear back so suddenly? She felt strangely vulnerable atop the temple, exposed. Once, such an idea would never have occurred to her.

She could be seen so easily, watched without her being aware of it. At the thought, a spine tingling chill swept through her.

Below her she saw nothing more ominous than the spendid gray stone wonders of Chichén Itzá thrusting upward from the tangled overgrowth of lush foliage, the trampled green lawns that stretched between the temples and the ballcourt, and the narrow path etched through the encroaching jungles, that shady well-worn path that snaked to the sacrificial well. The last of the day's tourists were straggling toward their buses on their way back toward Merida or Cancun. Swarthy Mexicans in official uniforms were strutting about. There was no cause for alarm.

And then she saw *him*.

Beneath the Temple of the Warriors, a man was standing in the long shadow of one of the pillars in the Plaza of the Thousand Columns. He was staring up at her through binoculars. Perhaps with magnification he saw her looking down at him; perhaps he observed the widening of her eyes or that she'd suddenly paled. Whatever the cause, he dropped the binoculars and let them dangle from their black strap against his chest, and he stepped boldly out into the sun, staring up at her openly.

Her fear was instantly forgotten, and in its place a low rage simmered in her veins. He did not seem to mind her awareness of him; rather she thought he welcomed it. He was the same infuriatingly arrogant man who had been watching her all afternoon. Earlier, when she'd noticed those onyx dark eyes shaded by the longest of lashes, the blackest eyes she'd ever seen, fixed avidly on her person, she'd blushed and looked away. Stefano's camera had been clicking wildly, capturing her look of ingenue confusion, the same expression her ex-husband Enrico had long ago captured, launching her career and making her an instant celebrity in the crazy fashion world that loved such meteoric successes.

Stefano had begged repeatedly for that look again, but Andrea had been unable to duplicate it in the absence of the man with the smoke-dark eyes who had mysteriously vanished. Later, he'd reappeared when she was wearing almost nothing, only a wisp of daring white silk molding the delicate swell of her small bosoms and her slim body.

The man's insolent black gaze had stripped away white silk, and inexplicably she'd gone warm all over, her color deepening—this time with fury. She'd read his expression with the uncanny accuracy of a girl who'd grown up with an unruly thatch of curly carrot-red hair, freckles and braces, a strangely awkward girl too tall and too skinny to interest the high school boys of her class. How many times had such swift male appraisals, pregnant with that same vague, speculative contempt, left her feeling ashamed that she was not more desirable.

When she was twelve Andrea had stood two inches taller than any boy her own age. She'd marveled at the

other smaller, prettier girls, wishing with all her heart
that she could be like them. Their feet were small, their
hands tiny. Even their gestures were dainty. And their
breasts . . . they actually had breasts.

Those girls had mastered every trick of flirtation
while Andrea had continued to grow even taller.
They'd looked *up* through their long, thick, fluttering
lashes at the boys, while Andrea's wrists had hung two
awkward inches past the cuffs of her sleeves. Her jean
hems had dangled those same two inches above her
ankles and enormous feet, so that she always looked as
if she were sprouting out of her clothes, giving the
effect of a female Li'l Abner.

Gawky, skinny, miserably lacking in sex appeal and
self-confidence, Andrea had been forced to search
inside herself for survival skills. She'd found intelli-
gence, artistic talent, sensitivity to the needs of others,
and a never-failing sense of humor to carry her through
those awful years. She'd grown so interested in things
outside herself, so self-sufficient, that she hadn't even
noticed the moment she became—what was it everyone
said about her—"interesting to look at." Enrico, alone,
had seen.

The cool glance of this dark stranger brought back so
many agonized moments in her life, all those terrible
feelings of inadequacy she'd experienced because she
looked more like a beanpole than an hourglass, because
her delicately boned, freckled face with enormous
green eyes and too-full lips lacked classical perfection.
For years it had goaded her that men—men like this
particular dark and, no doubt, shallow, macho male—
desired only small, rounded women, women with full
breasts and shapely curves.

Andy stared down at the man, her rage growing. It
had taken her a long time to realize that a woman was
more than just a body or a pretty face. That she wasn't
a nobody because her looks weren't perfect, that there

were different kinds of beauty. And, of course, it had helped her self-confidence immensely when Enrico with his rare genius had discovered her and shown the world that her face, for all its obvious flaws, was arrestingly beautiful.

But if this stranger found her so unattractive, why did he keep watching her?

Earlier Andrea had dismissed the man's interest. People frequently gawked at models and photographers during shootings. Sometimes a fellow might linger and attempt to flirt. But he hadn't done that. Somehow this man was different.

He was interested in her—only in her, not in the others. And yet, despite the obvious intensity of his interest, there was no sexual element in it, rather a vague hostility. She was sure she was right about him thinking her flat-chested and skinny, not his sort at all. Why then his obvious interest? Suddenly she was curious as well as deeply bothered by him, and she longed to stomp down the steps of the temple and confront him.

He was quite tall, and he stood very straight. His black hair that he wore fairly long, just the way she liked a man to wear his hair, the way Don wore his, shone in the golden light, and the faint breeze ruffled it across his brow and against the edges of his collar. He was attractive in a vitally male way; it was something she'd felt in every treacherous, female bone of her body the first moment her eyes had met his, just as she'd known she was not the sort of woman he found attractive.

Stefano, who had his camera together again, began rapidly calling out instructions, expecting from her that instant, professional obedience that was a characteristic of hers. The makeup artist rushed up to retouch her face.

"Bella, tonight there is a fire in you I want to capture

on film. Give me all that warmth and beauty. Make your eyes flash. You're real and alive. Think glamor. Let that gorgeous mane of red hair burn down your back."

"Ah, yes," Andrea sighed, tossing her hair in a wildly dramatic manner. "Burn is right!" The thick heat was at last getting to her, and the fur felt so suffocating she could hardly breathe. She chuckled zestily. "I'm a woman afire in the jungle because I'm an idiot who brought nothing to wear but this fur." *Think glamor, glamor, glamor,* she told herself, *and not that I'm roasting alive on this great, gray slab.* As always she marveled at how utterly ridiculous this business could be. She laughed for the camera as she moved.

For the moment the mysterious man below, as well as her own inexplicable attack of nerves, was forgotten. She forced her most dazzling smile, that same dazzling smile that had graced nearly two hundred covers of the world's most renowned fashion magazines. Her extraordinarily expressive face seemed to catch a thousand nuances as Stefano's camera enthusiastically clicked. She wrapped the fur about her body as though the feel of it against her skin was the most sensual of pleasures. Then she unwrapped it slowly, her every movement seductive. Somehow, on her, even in the baking summer heat, that fur looked absolutely luscious, the most desirable of garments. She had that rare quality, so essential in a photographic model, called camera presence. On film she was a stunning and charismatic beauty, able to intuitively transfer her own appeal to whatever she was wearing.

Race Jordan sucked in a deep breath as he stared up at the woman with the hair of flame and the body as graceful and pliant as warm rubber as she molded herself to that ancient statue, and then withdrew only to drape herself upon it again. The seductive movements of her body made him think of the sexual act, and he felt she was deliberately teasing him.

She was bouncing up and down upon the statue now, her expression ecstatic. A wild heat flushed his face, and he swiped at the perspiration on his brow. What in the hell was happening to him? He didn't go for skinny women.

It was only the jungle, of course, the humidity of the tropics getting to him. Not the woman or what she was doing, he told himself; but still, he couldn't pull his eyes off that graceful undulating body. He couldn't stop himself from wondering how she would feel molded tightly against him. Her waist was small, just right for a man's hand. She had long shapely legs, and though she was extremely slender, she moved with feminine grace.

He disliked her, of course, and everything she represented, everything she threatened, he reminded himself quickly. Yet, when he attempted to shoot her a savage glance, the feelings she engendered were no longer as hostile as before.

She was stripping out of the fur, slowly, seductively. She wore only a filmy bit of diaphanous chiffon. The breeze caught the flimsy gown, curling it around her golden body, revealing curving legs and creamy thighs. He watched the soft fabric ripple over the taut peaks of her small, yet firm and shapely breasts. A muscle twitched in his jaw. He was acutely conscious of the spreading ache in his loins. She was setting him on fire. He didn't want to keep looking at her, but he couldn't stop himself.

She was laughing now, her head thrown back, her hair falling silkily like a scarlet veil over her shoulders. She arched her back, accentuating every feminine curve, and then she began bouncing again. Her small breasts jutted upward, then moved, jiggling faintly with her movements. The skirt fluttered upward; the curve of luscious hip was wantonly displayed as she knelt and pulled the fur playfully across one shoulder.

She had changed positions and was crawling on all fours on top of the fur. Her head was bent down so that her thick mane of hair swung against the stone idol and the luxuriant fur. Race imagined the woman's slight body poised in such a position on top of his, her hair swaying across his face, her thighs spread apart to accommodate his body. He would have pulled her down . . . down . . . He could almost feel the hot, moist tightness of her eager body.

Suddenly he could stand it no longer. He did not want to desire her; he had not followed her to Chichén Itzá for that. With one violent movement he tore his gaze from the intoxicating vision and strode from the temple toward the concession stands.

When the shooting was over, Andrea noted at once that the handsome dark stranger had disappeared. She felt vaguely disappointed, though she wouldn't admit this to herself. She shed her fur and high heeled boots and stepped into her own sneakers so that she could carefully descend the Mayan temple. Five minutes later she dashed inside the bright blue van Stefano had rented and ripped off her false eyelashes. Mercilessly she scrubbed her face so clean that every freckle showed. Then she changed into her own faded jeans and a light summer blouse.

She just had an hour to explore the ancient ballcourt before Stefano and the others would be ready to leave, and she was enthusiastic to at least have a look at it and perhaps to do a few sketches.

When Andrea reached the ballcourt she stood on the edge of the sheer vertical wall and reverently contemplated the ancient ruin, almost gasping in admiration. She began reading the little guide book she'd bought which said that the ballcourt at Chichén Itzá was the largest and finest ballcourt ever discovered, that the two parallel walls were 272 feet long separated by a playing field 199 feet wide, that the vertical walls were exactly 27 feet high with two circular stone rings set 23 feet from the ground in each of the facing walls. She read also that the object of the game was thought to have been to get the ball through those rings, that the winners of the game received all the jewelry, adornments and apparel of the spectators, that the losers were probably decapitated, that this game had been a religious rite of the Toltecs.

Slowly she stopped reading, folding her guide book and stuffing it into her pocket while she gazed at the magnificent wonder of the ruin. There was something so eerily mysterious about ancient civilizations, and they deeply fascinated her. She could feel the power of the past more keenly when she came to places like this. She no longer felt quite so constrained by the pressures of her twentieth century, hustle-bustle lifestyle. She felt free in some nebulous space in time. Always she felt compelled by a consuming curiosity. She tried to imagine the lives and fates of those who played this game, the daily lives of the spectators who came to a game where they would be obliged to give up all they had brought or worn.

At last she sat down, folding one slender denim clad knee over the other, letting her leg dangle over the wall as she began one of her surrealistic sketches. With bold, sloping strokes she drew the ballcourt filled with players and people. Looming from the center of the page and by far the largest image on her pad, the ball was soaring toward one of the stone rings in the wall. In the middle of the ball she unerringly sketched a face—the dark, boldly handsome features of the man who'd been watching her all day.

The movements of her charcoal were rapid and sure. A few black dashes had caught, with amazing accuracy, not only the details of his appearance—the rumpled thickness of his hair sweeping low across his high forehead, the thick brows slanting above wide-set, black eyes, the long thin nose with its flaring nostrils, and those masculine, sensually-full lips—but caught something of the man himself. There was an unmistakable cool recklessness in the arch of an arrogant brow, a delicious danger in the cynical twist of his smile.

She started to sketch the man's body, but as she imagined the bronzed flesh and hard muscle, as she imagined herself held tightly against him, her body touching his, her fingers began to tremble.

Absently she drew another picture, and again the man's features dominated it. She was just finishing it when a long shadow fell across her tablet, darkening it. Her hand with the bit of charcoal in it froze. Frightened, she whirled around.

Her vision was filled by the tall black shape of a man, legs thrust widely apart, towering over her, dominating her, the very same man she'd been sketching. Instantly she jumped up, blushing prettily, wildly dropping her tablet and scattering her bits of charcoal onto the ground in her confusion. More slowly, as if to deny her agitation, she grabbed a rag and hastily cleaned her hands.

"I didn't mean to startle you," he said.

But, of course, that was exactly what he'd meant to do.

She heard no apology in his deeply melodious drawl. His was the most beautiful and most masculine of voices, strong and sure like the man himself, and its husky sound seemed to vibrate though every nerve ending in her body as though he were caressing her with it.

"I . . . actually you didn't startle me. I was just getting ready to go. . . . The others will be expecting me . . ."

She felt dazed by his presence, as though she were in a state of shock.

One dark eyebrow arched quizzically, mercilessly. "Will they?" he mocked, his disbelief evident in his deep tone.

Desperately she cocked her head, trying to look past him. She was lying, of course, and it was obvious he saw how blatantly. If he had so much as a shred of common courtesy he would have at least pretended to believe her, she thought irritably. She despised herself for stammering like a frightened child. She hadn't felt this flustered in years. What was it about this maddening man?

He was so stunningly charismatic—an annoying but very excited little voice at the back of her mind whispered.

The sun was directly behind him, painting her beauty with its glowing light, shining in the red-gold softness of her cascading curls, rendering her flashing green eyes jewel-brilliant, tinting her skin with its golden radiance. He stared down at her in that boldly unnerving way of his, smiling slightly as though he had decided she was not nearly so unattractive as he'd originally thought.

There was an impertinence in his intent expression that made her feel both feminine pleasure that he was so obviously interested in her as well as embarrassment that perhaps she wasn't wearing enough. She was suddenly as keenly aware of her nipples thrusting against her thin shirt as he was, of the tightness of her jeans. She flushed, bristling. He had no right to look at her as though he owned her. For no reason at all her heart began to pound.

She forced herself to give him look for look. Boldly her gaze traveled slowly up pressed denim jeans that clung like an outer layer of skin to the man's smoothly muscled thighs. What did he do—ride horses all day?

He was so tall, so much taller than she'd realized,

dwarfing her, and she was a tall woman. For a treacherous moment she savored the pleasant and novel sensation of feeling small herself, tiny and delicately feminine.

He was a magnificent specimen of a man with no surplus flesh to mar the lean perfection of his body, his skin tanned dark from the sun. His shoulders were thick with powerful muscle, his waist narrow, his stomach flat. He wore a crisp, sky-blue shirt casually open at the throat and tucked neatly in at the waist.

Something about him overwhelmed her—his very nearness. She went warm all over, as if she'd stepped dangerously close to a roaring fire and been set aflame. But when she would have backed away, he moved toward her swiftly, his great body lazily graceful, though his expression was suddenly charged with an urgency she didn't understand. He pulled her easily into his arms. She felt herself pressed against the toughest male body she'd ever felt.

She gasped, her response to his touch instantaneous, like the combustion of match striking flint. A bolt of shocking white heat went through her, and she was melting in his arms as wax near flame. Suddenly she was trembling against the hard masculine flesh enveloping her, her fingertips nervously aflutter against his powerful chest. She was only vaguely aware of the pleasant whiff of his cologne, of the appealing fragrance of his own clean, masculine scent. She was more conscious of the fiery power of the man.

Race savored the feel of her body against the hardness of his. He remembered her sensual movements atop the Mayan temple, and how then he'd ached to hold her. Well, he was holding her now, learning the warmth of her, the wild responsiveness of her, the mysterious attraction she held for him. His heart began to pound, and his body responded to the womanliness of her, putting him in an acute state of male need. It took all his willpower not to knead the soft flesh of her breasts with his fingers, not to ravage her upturned mouth with his own; he knew he wanted to taste her, to feel her, to possess her.

She was shockingly aware of his urgent male arousal. Andrea's long-lashed eyes lifted to his in startled wonder, before she at last managed to speak in a strangely breathless voice.

"Just what do you think you're doing? Let me go-o." She tried to back farther away and the heel of her sneaker slid precariously over the edge of the thirty foot wall, and for the first time she sensed her dangerous position. She clung to him then, her heart beating jerkily.

He held her so tightly it was as if their flesh was fused together.

He smiled down at her. His deep voice was husky. "Let you go so you can break your neck . . ." he remarked dryly, his warm breath a disturbingly sensuous sensation against her temple. He held her for a long moment, longer than necessary, pressing her against himself, as though he relished the feel of her surprisingly soft body pressing so earnestly against his. "It's not what I'm doing, but what you're doing to me that alarms you, little one." He laughed softly into her hair so that again she felt the warmth of his breath. At last he drew her away from the edge to safety, and released her, leaving her with a bewildering sensation of disappointment. "Next time—watch where you're going," he advised, "though I didn't mind saving you. Not in the least. Anytime. . . . In fact I don't even need an excuse."

There was laughter in his dark eyes as well as another emotion that kindled a wave of answering heat in her own body.

"I didn't imagine that you did." Still, her body felt afire, and the sensation was far more enjoyable than she would have admitted.

His black gaze devoured her, stripping away her clothes. "You're no different. I watched you on the temple. Wasn't that a deliberate turn-on?" Something alive and vital in his expression challenged her spirit.

"For the camera—yes. Not you."

"Ah, but I was watching. You're very good at your work." He was smiling as though he'd immensely enjoyed observing her.

"Who are you? What do you want?"

"I want to talk to you—among other things." There was a deliberate suggestive note in that last that made her aware of primeval male as well as female urges.

He was kneeling to retrieve her tablet from the ground. When she realized with horror that he would no doubt see her sketches, she made an agitated rush toward the tablet herself. But he was far swifter than she.

He lifted the tablet from the ground, flipping the long pages as he studied her drawings. She watched in mortification as the tanned skin beneath his eyes crinkled slightly with ill-suppressed amusement, as that eyebrow of his that liked to arch, arched. A slow grin spread across his handsome features as his black gaze swung to her reddening face.

"Give me that," she snapped, reaching for the notebook.

"Not so fast." He swerved, holding the tablet just out of her reach. His black eyes twinkled. "It isn't every day I discover I'm the subject of such a gifted lady's admiration."

"You . . . you are not the subject of my admiration." she croaked. "I detest you for being so rude and forward and for holding me like that, letting me know that you . . . that I . . ."

"That you attract me. At least we're in no doubt about the state of my admiration for you." His black eyes were twinkling.

She felt desperate to change the subject. "Those are private pictures that I had no intention of showing anyone . . . and you shouldn't have taken them after I asked you not to."

"Curiosity is only one of the many weaknesses in my rather flawed, shall I say, character—as you will discover when you know me better," he replied softly, not in the least chagrined over his abominable behavior.

"There isn't the slightest chance of our getting to know one another better," she hissed.

His knowledgeable gaze flicked over her. "We shall see." He smiled that very white smile that made him so devilishly attractive, that smile that sent an unwanted ripple of heat throughout her body.

Oooh. His conceit was scarcely endurable. His actions and manner those of a determined blockhead. She was suddenly so furious both with him and with herself for feeling even vaguely attracted by his dark good looks that she wanted to chew nails. Damn the man. She searched her mind for an insult vile enough to drive him away, but her imagination proved inadequate to the task. It was strangely difficult to think in his presence. "You're simply not the kind of person I want to know," she said at last in an odd, low voice. "Curiosity is the least of your faults."

He was studying her pictures with great interest, and listening to her with much less. "Really?" he murmured absently.

"You intrude where you're not wanted. You're a spy, a voyeur, and a sneak. You take things that don't belong to you," she persisted heatedly.

He glanced toward her, not in the least angered as she'd hoped he would be. When he spoke his voice was smoothly pleasant. "As I said before—curiosity is my greatest weakness, and I was curious about you. I wanted to see what you were drawing."

"Even though I didn't want you to?"

His eyes flashed. *"Particularly* for that reason." Again he smiled that maddeningly knowing smile that forced her to grit her teeth to maintain even a degree of control. "Besides, good pictures are meant to be shared, and these are good."

Just as she was beginning to bask smugly at his praise, despite her efforts to remain indifferent, he added a left-handed tail to his compliment that completely took the wind out of her sails. ". . . for an amateur."

"Who are you to judge my work?" she fumed.

"I know quite a bit about art," he replied evasively, noting the high color in her cheeks as well as the quivering of her tightly compressed lips. "Enough to see that you are a fervent admirer of Salvador Dali. Perhaps too fervent."

"What do you mean?" Her interest was caught.

"That an artist must be careful to find his own style."

They lapsed into silence and he returned his attention to her first sketch, studying it closely. He lifted his black head, and she found herself studying the blue-black ribbons glistening in the thick waves of his hair. "On second thought, maybe my original interpretation was a little conceited," he murmured on a deliberately rueful note, as though he came to this conclusion with the deepest regret. Sparkling dark eyes met hers with an avidity that seemed to touch her soul. "My head in this ball—thank God you don't have it dripping blood. Does this express a secret desire to decapitate me?" He looked at her again, again with those brilliant amused eyes. "Perhaps there's a bit of the savage Toltec maiden in you after all. I like wild women, and they usually like me."

His dark gaze raked her, and she felt the power of him as though it pulsed through the marrow of her bones. His awesome virility was like an overpowering force. Suddenly she found herself thinking of him and wild women, of hot wanton caresses, of volatile male-female sensations, and a hot emotion flared inside her. She didn't want to react to him. She didn't want to be drawn to him. He was a stranger.

"I don't doubt that for a minute," she burst violently, and then choked on this admission as he began to laugh. She stared at him furiously, helplessly, completely at a loss for words, wishing in vain that he would simply disappear.

"I'm glad your only weapon was a piece of charcoal then," he said, assuming from her deepening scowl that she might have severed his head had she been able. "I'll know to stay clear of you when you're chopping wood with an axe or cleaning a gun."

"I don't chop wood or own a gun," she retorted icily, snatching her tablet from him.

"Knowing that, I'll sleep easier, nights." His expression was as teasing as a small boy's; it was clear he wasn't in the least afraid of her or of anyone else. He was obviously enjoying himself immensely at her expense.

Suddenly she smiled in spite of herself, simply because the man's sheer magnetism was irresistible. The thought formed warily in the back of her mind that she'd never been so deeply nor so quickly, drawn to any man as she was to this impertinent stranger, infuriating as he was. Not even to Enrico and, of course, never to Don.

Enrico had swept her into marriage in a blaze of passion, a blaze that had gone out almost as quickly as it had been ignited, leaving in its place only the ashes of disillusionment. Their brief marriage had left Andrea with a deep distrust for the durability of sexual chemistry, no matter how powerful, between a man and a woman. That was why when she'd begun to think seriously about a man again, it had been a man whose personality and mind appealed to her. Her relationship with Don was based on a deep friendship and shared interests rather than physical attraction.

"You have a beautiful smile," the stranger said softly, his admiring gaze lingering on her moist, half-parted lips as though their sweetness tempted him.

She felt strangely aglow for the fleeting instant she involuntarily responded to his compliment. Some rebel part of herself wanted him to be attracted to her. Her gentle face was radiant with pleasure, and he was deeply touched by the soft beauty in her expression.

With an effort she suppressed a curious, magic sensation of discovery, hardening herself against him, reminding herself that he was probably a man who knew how to charm women, like Enrico, a man who would lead any woman on even if she only vaguely attracted him, if he saw anything in it for himself.

"Save that line, along with all the others in what is I'm sure a great repertoire, for some more desperate and more gullible woman," she said crisply. "Poor, foolish soul," she finished pityingly, remembering how her own heart had been broken with just such insincerities. "It's getting late, and you've wasted enough of my time—and yours. The others are probably waiting for me at the van."

Turning her back to him in haughty dismissal, she stooped and began gathering her art materials. But he did not leave despite her rebuff. Instead he leaned down beside her and began to help her retrieve her belongings. She was too sharply aware of crisp blue cloth stretching across the muscular expanse of his shoulders. Rudely she snatched the items he solicitously handed her.

"They're not waiting!" he said with calculated mildness, dropping the last bit of charcoal into her box with a *plunk,* raising his black, intense gaze to her face. When her startled eyes lifted to his, he explained himself without a trace of conscience. "I told them not to, that I would drive you back to your hotel."

"You what?" She went hot suddenly, like a brilliant star, tensing inside like a coiled ball of fury.

"You heard me," he returned casually, not in the least perturbed, finding to his surprise that he was enjoying her passionate anger that was so easily aroused. Until this moment Race Jordan had never liked temper in women. But it was but part of the alluring fire in this woman.

The artist in him had seen at once that her face, for all its faults, would be an interesting subject to paint. Her hair was as vivid as flame against the paleness of her skin. But it was the boldness in her eyes that fascinated him, the boldness of her movements, that gave her an aura of sensuality, this boldness so distinctly at variance with her freshly scrubbed girl-next-door face and her almost non-existent female curves.

But there was fire in her. He wondered suddenly if there was softness as well.

Race let his black gaze roam over her slim body with ravaging intensity. What he saw did not displease him.

She was slender—much too slender to suit his usual taste in women, and her breasts seemed scarcely more than gentle swells of soft flesh. But in spite of these obvious defects he found her very desirable, more desirable in fact than any woman in a very long time. This thought gave him pause; he did not *want* to like anything about her. But he couldn't seem to stop himself.

Suddenly he realized that he hadn't been in the least attracted to her until he'd watched her during her shooting atop the Mayan temple. Then he'd come upon her and spoken to her, and she'd reacted explosively to him. She'd been so charmingly flustered when he'd caught her drawing him, and when he'd seized her in his arms and felt her trembling body against his own, something vital and electric had leapt from her to him, and suddenly his desire had intensified. He'd been filled with the hot need to feel the moist softness of her lips beneath his own, to possess this slim fiery creature so unlike all the previous women in his life. It was simply her, her spirited essence that he wanted, and he was bewildered by the intensity of this need.

Race caught himself abruptly and drew his gaze back to her arresting face. She was not his sort, not at all. He'd seen that from the first. Whatever he was feeling was no more than the novelty of encountering a woman so different from all the other women he'd known. It would doubtless pass quickly. He liked soft, dark, feminine women with sweet, yielding dispositions, gentle passive creatures with whom he could easily have his way. But he now understood how Don had gotten himself into this jam. This woman was as wild and dangerously vital as an explosion of dynamite, and Don's life had been so tedious and difficult that he'd needed a diversion like this redheaded firecracker.

Race realized she intrigued him, but he'd allowed that mysterious affinity he felt toward her to divert him from his purpose too long. His expression hardened imperceptibly.

Andrea's mind reeled. She stared at Race as though he were a three-headed monster. This stranger had actually told Stefano and the others to leave without her. "I can't believe you had the audacity, that you actually . . ." She stopped talking. She *could* believe it; she did. She found her voice again, and it sounded strangely hoarse, not like her own at all. "What gave you the right to do something like that? You had no reason . . ."

"Oh, I had a reason," he said so nonchalantly she longed to slap him.

She stared questioningly at him, so enraged she didn't trust herself to speak.

"This might be my last chance to stop you from seeing Don tonight," he said coldly, thoroughly shocking her. His gaze had hardened imperceptibly, and an icy chill swept through her. Never had it occurred to her that this man might be in any way connected with Don. Her face paled suddenly to the bloodless hue of dry bone.

"Who are you? How did you know about Don and me—when our relationship is a secret?"

"Of course your relationship is a secret, and that's how I want to keep it," Race said, his low tone somehow menacing.

Don had been adamant about keeping their relationship private, Andrea thought, but she'd believed that was only because he was a Congressman and she a celebrity in her own right. Always he'd taken her to out-of-the way places where they wouldn't be photographed.

Who was this man who had found out? What did it mean? Suddenly she was remembering the late night phone calls, the whispered warnings, the car that had almost run her down.

A tiny dull hammer began to pound in her temple. She knew without knowing that this determined man would be a powerful adversary, that the shining new happiness she'd thought she'd found with Don was threatened.

"But how did you find out about us? And why do you care?" It was an effort to keep her voice from trembling. There was so much about Don she didn't understand, so much of himself he'd kept from her, so much she'd hoped to learn by coming to Mexico and seeing him.

"That's what we'll talk about on the way back to Cancun, Miss Ford," Race answered cryptically. "Ready?"

Chapter 2

RACE'S STEEL GRIP TIGHTENED ON HER ELBOW AS HE helped her arise. The expression on his handsome face was implacable.

Andrea wanted to kick out at him, to stomp, to scream, but one look at his powerful male body told her how silly and fruitless such childish actions would be. He would effortlessly subdue her. She lifted her smoldering gaze to his, but then, thinking better of her tack of open rebellion, she allowed her burnished lashes to flutter demurely downward. It was a coy gesture, and Race observed it with suspicion.

Perhaps she'd been handling this man all wrong.

"I . . . I don't even know your name . . ." she murmured softly, forcing an uncertain smile.

She was acting more like the women he was used to. He thought her very beautiful when she smiled, for her lips were voluptuously full, her slightly but prettily crooked teeth very white. Her eyes shone as though lit with an inner radiance, and for an instant he felt his guard slip.

"Race Jordan."

His deep voice vibrated through her.

"And mine is . . ."

"I know yours."

"You know all about me," she said quietly, "while I know nothing about you. That gives you an unfair advantage."

He did not deny his knowledge. "It's always wise to have an unfair advantage over one's enemies," he returned dryly.

Green eyes slanted up at him, and she was struck by the heat of his gaze. "I'm not your enemy," she murmured shakily.

In that moment he wished that what she said was true; he thought her an enchantress with her brilliant hair flowing about her delicate face, her smile so engaging, her eyes glowing, and her every graceful curve revealingly displayed to him by her skin-tight clothes. His eyes wandered over her in frank male appraisal.

"Race." He liked the way she said his name, the sensuous sound of it a velvet-softness on her lips.

"Hmmm." He looked down at her, marveling at this new docility. But then, he didn't really know her. Perhaps hers was a mercurial nature. Or perhaps she was simply practical and had decided to make the best of the situation. Deep in the recesses of his mind the disturbingly pleasant thought formed that maybe she didn't dislike the prospect of being alone with him as much as she'd said she did.

With difficulty she forced her hand to tentatively reach out and touch his arm. He felt her fingers hovering warm and vibrantly light above his flesh; this gesture was somehow provocative. Then she curled her trembling fingertips around the granite hardness of his forearm, and each became even more acutely aware of the treacherous allure of touching the other.

"Would you mind helping me down those steps," she whispered meekly, her sweet smile masking the turbulence of her true emotions. "I've always been so afraid of heights." She hoped he didn't hear that faint strangling sound bubbling in her throat, and she was careful to keep her eyes downcast so he could not see their blazing fire.

He shot her a quick look, his curiosity suddenly aroused. He had a vivid recollection of her scampering lightly down the steep side of the Temple of the Warriors with the fearless agility of a mountain goat. And where had her fear been when she'd been sitting on the edge of the thirty foot wall, drawing those violent, absurd sketches? Nevertheless he was intrigued by this new gentleness in her. Besides, he liked the feel of her slim body against his as well as the pleasant sensation of her soft hand clinging to his arm.

"Of course I don't mind," he said gallantly. "I'll carry your sketch pad and charcoals."

"Would you?" She smiled gratefully up at him, all the time her mind a savage turmoil behind the sweetness of her face.

On the last step she stumbled, and the hard warmth of his arms immediately drew her slim body against his own. She felt the tough male virility of him in every pore of her body, and she involuntarily responded as though she were a wanton. Her pulse pounded its song of desire; she flushed before she pushed him quickly away, and he helped her down the last step.

From behind her she heard his deep and very infuriating chuckle.

This couldn't be happening, Andrea screamed silently as he led her toward the gray steps so they could descend to the lawn. She felt she was being abducted by a perfect stranger, and for what sinister purpose she wouldn't let herself imagine. She knew only that she was in danger, that Don himself might be in danger, and she had to do something; she had to think of some way to extricate herself from this impossible situation. But what?

The green sweep of lawn was now deserted, the massive stone archeological structures silent, the distant parking lot empty. The sky was darkening rapidly. She stared desolately at the exact spot where Stefano's blue van had been parked, feeling betrayed that the others had taken the word of this stranger and abandoned her.

Race's strides were long, and despite her own long legs she felt rushed as he pulled her along. When they reached the parking lot, he led her to a white Volkswagen and unlocked the door, helping her inside. She noted the car rental papers on the dash and other papers scattered on the backseat. Race was moving lithely around the front of the car and opening his door. She watched every move he made. He dropped the keys onto the dashboard and swung one leg into the cramped quarters of the car. She wondered desperately if she should leap from her own door and make a run for it. Perhaps she could hide in the jungle until he gave up searching for her. But even if she escaped him, she would be alone in Mexico, miles from the nearest town, at the mercy of strangers who might prove more dangerous than he. Though she spoke scarcely a word of Spanish, she knew enough about Mexico to know that she was probably safer with this man than she would be by herself.

Out of the corner of her eye she saw a white car circle slowly into the lot. She read *Policia* on the side of the vehicle, and her heart pounded with new hope. Ironically, Race seemed to think of something he needed to ask the men in the car, and he called to the officers in

Spanish. Negligently he pulled himself back out of the car and began speaking fluently in Spanish.

Andrea stared fixedly at the two silver keys on the dash. Her heart began to thump. If only she dared.

A fat, officious Mexican officer who swabbed his brow continually with a white handkerchief had gotten out of his car, and was now talking heatedly to Race, pointing down the highway toward Mérida as though to explain something. Reluctantly Race moved toward the officer, leaving the car and the woman in it unattended. He glanced back at her a couple of times, and then became so absorbed in what the officer was saying that he turned his back to her.

Slowly Andrea slid into the driver's seat and inserted the key into the ignition. There was an icy coldness in the pit of her stomach as she bent her left arm over the steering column and twisted the key. Her palms were clammy. She clasped the gear shift awkwardly with her right hand.

Andrea drew a deep breath in a vain attempt to steady her nerves. Because she had lived in Manhattan so long she no longer had a car or even a valid driver's license, and she hadn't driven in nearly eight years.

There was a lull in the men's conversation, and the Mexican officer turned to go back to his patrol car, while Race headed toward her. In another moment, Andrea's chance would be lost.

Without a flicker of hesitation she switched on the engine, shifted grindingly into the wrong gear, and the Volkswagen lurched forward in with bucking, jolting motions. The car jumped like a sickly beetle toward the highway that cut through *chicle* plantations and jungle to Cancun. And freedom.

Behind her Race let out a gutteral cry of surprise, and ran toward the jerking car just as the police vehicle swung onto the gravel drive beneath the trees that led to Chichén Itzá. Race almost caught up with Andrea just as she jammed the gear shift into first and sped away from him.

In her rearview mirror Andrea saw Race, and she relished with childish glee the look of stunned surprise and blazing anger on his dark face as a smothering curl of thick, choking dust from the unpaved parking lot enveloped him. In a rage he slammed her sketching tablet onto the ground, and suddenly she began to giggle with delight. Though she knew it was probably unwise, she couldn't resist the impulse to tap a little farewell toot on her horn and fling her arm out the window and wave a jaunty goodbye. It was one of those rare, unexpected moments in her life when she tasted the richly delicious flavor of triumph.

Race stood in the parking lot and watched the Volkswagen's taillights until they were a weaving flicker disappearing into the gloom. Then his furious gaze fell to the tablet at his feet. The pages had blown open to reveal that surreal picture she'd drawn of his head in the ball. His own cynical smile leapt from the page to mock him.

He stared blindly down at the picture. Very slowly a broad grin spread across Race's handsome features, and his anger evaporated. He threw back his black head and roared a great, ringing, free laugh that carried into the jungle and filled its silence. He slapped his thigh and then knelt down and retrieved the tablet.

With a chuckle he remembered her artful submissiveness, and his own foolish, egotistical desire to think that perhaps she liked him just a bit and wasn't all that reluctant to drive back to Cancun alone with him. He'd miscalculated rather badly where that red-headed little termagant was concerned, he thought ruefully. Not *little,* he amended swiftly, remembering every delightful detail of her long-limbed loveliness. She was taller than most of the men he knew.

When he'd first discovered that Don was involved with her he'd assumed she was like other models he'd known in New York. That's where he'd made his first mistake. The other models of his acquaintance had been sweet young things who were so used to being pushed around by powerful agents, photographers and magazine editors that they'd never proved even the slightest challenge for his own much stronger personality. They'd been vain, ornamental creatures; not stupid any of them, rather single-minded of purpose, all of them driven to make it to the top in a racket he deplored for the superficiality of its values.

He thought of Andrea's freshly scrubbed face, every freckle showing on the slender bridge of that impudent nose of hers. He remembered her bargain-basement jeans and shabby blouse. Andrea Ford was neither vain nor ornamental. In fact, she wasn't particularly good looking—although, the male in him admitted, she was interesting to look at. Nor was she a sweet young thing, easily pushed around. She was well into her thirties, a woman with a mind of her own. He'd sensed a depth and a strength to her that astounded him, coming from one immersed in such a shallow business.

He thought of her sweet smile, of her arm clinging to his, and then sheepishly of his own male gullibility to her feminine wiles. She'd certainly cut him down to size. Hell, he must have been daft to have trusted her for even a second. But she'd seemed so damnably obliging there at the last. He found himself remembering the enchantment of her smile.

The police car which had driven onto the grounds of Chichén Itzá was once again pulling onto the lot. A sudden plan formed in Race's mind, and he threw out his arm and waved, signaling the police to wait as he began to jog toward them.

"Señores," he shouted when they seemed not to notice him.

The car ground to a standstill. A brown head stuck out of the window. *"Sí?"*

"Esperame, señores, por favor."

For an instant Race hesitated as he neared the car and was baffled by his own softness toward this extremely irritating woman. A vision as bizarre as one of the Ford girl's surrealistic pictures sprang to his mind. He imagined a desolate Andrea in manacles in a dingy Mexican jail. Then he pushed his absurd qualm of conscience aside.

The hell with her, Race thought, as his long deliberate strides carried him toward the men. He leaned casually against the police car, and smiled amiably down at the two swarthy men inside.

Let her tangle with the Mexican police for having stolen his rented car and see how she likes that. He could play the game as roughly as he had to; at all costs, he had to protect Linda and Don.

"Señores, favor de ayudarme con una problema."

Andrea hadn't gone a mile when the delirious glee at having escaped from Race Jordan receded, and the reality of her predicament sank in. Escape—to what? The thick trees that lined the narrow highway pressed close, and in the darkness they seemed vaguely menacing. A woman alone on a Mexican jungle road at night was scarcely safe. She would have to be exceedingly careful not to get herself into any further trouble.

The Volkswagen rattled along the rough highway, the combination of rental clients and Mexican roads having long ago obliterated its shocks. Andrea's long body was squashed uncomfortably in the tiny black seat, the steering wheel jammed against her rib-cage. Little cars weren't made for tall people, she thought miserably as one leg began to cramp.

She looked at the wobbly needle of the gas gauge and saw that there was half a tank. She was thankful at least for that, for suddenly she realized she'd left her purse, which contained the few pesos she'd brought with her, in Stefano's van. The rest of her money and her tourist card were at her hotel. She didn't have enough money to buy a tortilla much less a liter of gas. She had no driver's license, no identification of any kind. And she'd stolen—

Stolen. That's the first time she'd realized how Race might interpret her desperate flight from him. A new rush of anxiety swamped her, but she glued her eyes to the road and made no effort to turn the car around and go back. He had no right to do what he'd done, and she had every right to run from him. The fact that she was running in his car—well, that fact didn't bear thinking about.

Of one thing she was sure—she wasn't going back. Race Jordan was one man she never wanted to see again. He'd caused her more than enough trouble as it was. And devil that he was, he was probably just abominable enough to report that she'd stolen his car. It would be the obvious way of getting even with her for leaving him.

Andrea shivered with fear. The last thing she needed was to get into trouble with the law in Mexico. Still, her delicate chin remained stubbornly thrust forward, her toe pressed defiantly upon the accelerator, and she didn't regret what she had done. Though Race didn't look like a criminal, he had certainly been forcing her to go with him against her will. She'd been compelled to escape from him.

She wondered suddenly about Don. Why had Race been so determined to prevent her from seeing him, and how could he have known of her plans when she had confided them to no one?

A truck that had been trying to pass finally whizzed by, honking loudly. She became aware of the car that had been behind the truck zooming impatiently up behind her, its high white beam blinding her. There was another car trailing just as closely behind him.

Why can't these maniacs drive sanely? she thought desperately. Andrea clutched the steering wheel tightly as though she were hanging onto it with her life—which she was. She wasn't used to driving, and though she'd scarcely traveled more than a few kilometers, her nerves were in shreds. She felt as inadequate against these aggressive drivers as an unarmed soldier thrust suddenly into combat.

Every driver on the road seemed to be in a mad contest to pass the next car, and then the next. The worst of it was that if they saw another car they would race to catch up so they could tail it bumper to bumper at the highest possible speed. The slightest miscalculation in the lead car could easily cause a six-car accordion pileup. She would be lucky to get to Cancun alive.

Just for an instant she almost wished that a certain tall dark individual were driving, because she intuitively knew that he would be sure and fearless behind the wheel, even on this free-for-all racetrack filled with hellbent Mexican drivers.

It took Andrea two laborious hours to reach Cancun, and when she at last saw the rise of new white buildings and the glimmer of lights above the jungle treetops, she felt giddy with relief. She'd made it back to town, but what was she going to do with the car? She putted along toward her hotel thinking.

As she drove past the numerous exotic shops and boutiques along the palm-fringed streets, where only yesterday evening she had shopped with her friend Kim and the other models, all of them feeling lighthearted and carefree as they discovered such diverse items as Dutch cheeses and chocolates, French perfumes, Bavarian crystal, Italian leather and lots of designer-label couture, all available at bargain prices in the shops. Some of the biggest names in the world of high fashion had been represented in the colorful shops—Paco Rabanne, Givenchy and Christian Dior. She'd seen sportswear by Fila and Sergio Tacchini and jewelry by Piaget and Cartier. The free-port status of Cancun, as well as its jet-set clientele, obviously attracted merchants from all over the world.

Penny-pincher that she was, the only thing Andrea had bought was an attractive cotton *huipil* that she planned to wear as a beach cover-up, and a Caribbean black coral necklace. But she'd enjoyed browsing through the stacks of Panama hats and lacy hammocks as well as the crafts from other regions of Mexico: wood carvings, straw baskets, blankets, serapes, and tin and brass objects from Guanajuato, as well as pottery from Tonalá and Metepec.

Andrea was not thinking of the delights of yesterday's shopping spree, but rather of the pressing problem facing her tonight.

Suddenly in one of those blinding flashes of inspiration that she'd come to rely on to get her out of tight spots, she slowed the car and braked abruptly beside the clean-swept curb of Cancun Boulevard. In the distance she could see the modern, sloping shape of a great beachfront hotel that had been constructed to look like a Mayan pyramid. Beyond the curb, palm fronds swayed in the gentle sea breezes, and their dark shadows danced inside the car. But Andrea was not alert to her surroundings. Her forehead was furrowed in concentration as she reached for the rental car papers on the dash and began to study them, smiling for the first time since she'd left Race.

If she returned the car herself to the car rental agency, the car could not possibly be considered stolen. She breathed a deep sigh of relief as she thought this over. Carefully, she read the map and figured out the exact location of the agency. Luckily it was only a few blocks away.

A triumphant smile lit her face as she maneuvered the Volkswagen into the parking lot. She gathered all of Race's belongings into her arms and got out of the car, stretching to her full height. Every muscle in her body felt tight. Then she marched inside.

"I'd like to return Mr. Jordan's car," Andrea announced sweetly to a dark girl in lavender. Andrea placed the papers on the counter in front of the girl.

"*Pero,* but Señor Jordan, he just rented it today—for *nuestro* three-day special," the girl behind the desk explained, smiling. "Where is Mr. Jordan?" Her warm dark eyes flashed eagerly as though she remembered the handsome gringo. She had no doubt been looking forward to seeing him again.

"He's . . . not feeling so well. Montezuma's Revenge. . . ." More like Andrea's Revenge, she thought with a chuckle.

"I am so sorry. But it would be best if he brought the car back himself."

"I realize that," Andrea said evenly. "But he can't." The girl's luminous dark eyes were trained on Andrea's face, waiting. Andy gambled. "He's paying for it with a credit card, isn't he?" she asked ever-so-sweetly.

"*Sí, señorita.* We have his number and signature. He accidentally signed it in advance."

"Oh . . . he did?" The question was scarcely more than a murmur. Aloud she said, "Then bill him for the whole week."

The girl's eyes widened in surprise. "Are you sure this is the way he wants to handle it?"

"Very sure," Andrea purred warmly. "You see, Mr. Jordan feels that even though he no longer needs the car, he wants to do the honorable thing. He had intended to keep the car at least a week."

"What a very pleasant man he is."

"Yes," Andrea drawled, smiling dazzlingly at the girl. "Isn't he?"

Andy walked briskly out of the building, feeling suddenly very tired. She had risen before dawn to do her exercises and yoga and prepare herself for what had turned out to be an arduous shooting. She hadn't eaten in hours, and she was famished. It was nearly a mile to her hotel, but as she had not so much as a *centavo* for a taxi, she had no choice but to walk. Nevertheless, despite her hunger and exhaustion, despite the walk to be faced, she tossed her long red hair back so that it cascaded like rippling fire over her shoulders, and she began to laugh.

So much for an arrogant man who'd made the last few hours of her life memorably miserable. Perhaps he would think twice before he decided to play the bully with another unsuspecting young woman.

Andrea's jubilant mood quickly faded on that mile walk. She'd scarcely taken three steps when a truckload of young Mexican teenage boys began to follow her. They drove slowly beside her, so uncomfortably close that the tires of their truck almost brushed the curb. Brown arms hung like waving octopus tentacles from every open window. The boys shouted words in Spanish that Andrea suspected from their enthusiastic leers were either suggestive or obscene. Then they would laugh, their strident bravado making her feel cheap and unclean. Nevertheless she walked regally, her slim shoulders squared, her delicate nose tilted upward as she attempted to ignore them. But her cheeks were flushed with humiliation.

She thought of Race Jordan with fresh fury that grumbled through her like the simmering of a live volcano. If it hadn't been for that black-eyed bully she would long ago have eaten a sumptuous dinner in her hotel dining room—perhaps with Don. Or she might now be lazing in a tub of hot water, preparing for bed.

Suddenly she stumbled on a rock on the sidewalk,

almost falling. A savage pain shot through her slender
ankle as she twisted it. "Damn Race Jordan" she
muttered with vengeance. How she longed to pull
every hair, one by one, from that thick black crop of
hair until he yelled with pain.

"*Señorita . . . Chula.*" The sing-song Spanish
whirled around her as she quickened her pace despite
her ankle, fearful lest the boys decided to do more than
chant.

Oooh. There was no word in the English language
adequate to express her rage, her hatred at that man
who'd brought her so much discomfort.

At last she reached her hotel, and the truck zoomed
past her, wheeling back onto the main road, honking
loudly in jubilant farewell. She felt intensely relieved to
be safe, and she sagged against a white wall for a
moment to rest. Her ankle throbbed; her nerves were
frayed from having had to deal with those boys. But she
was safe, at least for the moment.

Her hotel was the most lavish in all of Cancun. It was
like a Mayan paradise. White sloping walls jutted
upward toward the black romance of a starlit sky.
Floodlights illuminated the gin-clear turquoise of the
lagoons and surf. The swimming pool glimmered like
an aqua jewel beneath mosaic columns. The soft,
melodious Mexican lovesongs floating from the bar
mingled with the boisterous sounds of laughter and the
hushed whispers between lovers in darkened corners.
But her beauteous surroundings were lost on her, as
though she were not a part of them.

Normally Andrea would have admired the lush tropi-
cal plants, the artistic landscaping of the hotel, the
building's magnificent architectural design. But she was
so upset her footsteps pattered hurriedly over the pastel
pink walkway, passing flower beds brimming thickly
with purple cane, skirting enormous ceramic pots that

dazzled with golden and scarlet crotons, overflowing ferns and palms. The exotic feathery orange blossoms on the poinciana trees moved faintly in the breeze.

She walked briskly past the hotel dining room with its delectable wafting aromas; she didn't want to eat alone in that romantic, darkened room with soft Spanish guitar music where she would be reminded that she wasn't with Don.

Andrea stayed in her hotel room only long enough to shower, change and toss everything she owned into her suitcase. Then she locked her door and headed quickly down the open-air corridor to her friend Kim's room.

Andrea would have preferred to spend the evening alone with her thoughts, but if she were sure of one thing, it was that the minute Race arrived in Cancun he would come to her hotel room. The last thing she wanted was another encounter with him, and she would not be there when he came knocking.

Pinching the thick folds of her lavender bathrobe together, though she hated to cover her long golden brown body, Kim swung the door of her hotel room open, and smiled her brightly-shy smile when she saw Andrea. Andrea had always thought Kim as exquisitely perfect as an oversized Barbie doll that lived and breathed with, though she was a sweet child, just about as much personality.

Kim's young face with her brilliant blue eyes was that of an angel, framed with flowing golden tresses. She was one of the newer models Luci had signed, and she was deeply in awe of Andrea. Luci had persuaded Andrea to take the younger model under her protective wing, and Andrea had done so because she felt sorry for her. New York was a big place for an eighteen-year-old girl from a small town. How well Andrea knew.

"Hey . . . hey . . . Andy, where's that handsome

dreamboat you left Chichén Itzá with?" Kim asked
teasingly, all youthful exuberance as she winked knowingly.

"Sunk beneath those aqua waves out there, curling
over the reef, even deeper than Davey Jones's locker, I
hope," Andy replied fervently, stepping inside her
friend's room and setting her suitcase down on the
waxed tile floor amid the colorful rumple of garments
Kim had carelessly strewn when she'd undressed earlier. Andrea was familiar with Kim's penchant for clut-
ter.

"You mean he isn't as good as he looks?" Kim
looked puzzled.

"Is any man?" Andy tossed evasively, feeling more
annoyed than usual by the girl's simplicity.

Andrea moved purposefully toward the bar, stepping
over a couple of glamour magazines that had fallen
from a disheveled assortment of reading material that
littered a low table. She felt vaguely irritated that Race
had so obviously charmed her young friend, but then
Kim wasn't too smart about men.

"Stefano told me you have my purse," Andrea said
dryly, hoping to change the subject.

"Over there." Kim pointed toward a brown clutch on
the littered bright purple sofa that was pushed against
an orange wall. "So what's the matter with Tall, Dark
and Handsome?"

"More than I care to go into at the moment."

"You're too cynical," Kim said. "You know that,
don't you?"

"You will be too, honey, when you're my age."

"You're only thirty-two."

"Don't rub it in, kid," Andy said wryly.

"Sorry."

Kim was very conscious of the difference in their
ages, and because age was desperately important to
her, signifying nothing more than sags and wrinkles,

she felt terrible to have reminded Andrea she wasn't so young as she used to be.

"Hey," Andrea said gently, seeing her distress. "It's okay. Getting older isn't *all* bad."

Kim stared at her blankly.

"I learned a lot in those fourteen years. You will, too."

Kim turned away, satisfied that at least Andy wasn't angry with her. She removed her robe to reveal her long-legged body clad only in the sheerest bra and panties. No doubt, Andrea mused indulgently, to admire herself; Kim was shamelessly conceited about her looks. The blond girl, who could never pass a silvered glass without pausing to preen in front of it like a parakeet, leaned toward the long mirror on the bathroom door and peered critically at her reflection. She frowned before she remembered that frowning made lines between her eyes. Moving closer, her attention zeroed in on a tiny blemish on her chin. "Oh dear," she moaned, genuine anguish in the soft sound. "I think I'm getting a pimple."

Andrea stuck her hand into a sack of chips on the bar and began to rummage. The sack, crisper than the chips, crackled. "Mind if I help myself? I'm starved."

"Mmmmm." Kim scarcely heard her, so intently was she studying the tiniest of specks beneath her lovely lips.

Taking the girl's mumble to mean she should help herself to food and drink, Andrea opened the refrigerator door and removed a bag of peanuts and a canned Coke. For a while she munched in silence, nibbling first on chips and then on the peanuts, watching Kim as she did so, heartily wishing Kim had something more substantial that she could eat. But unlike Andrea, who could eat like a truckdriver and never put on an inch, Kim had to constantly starve herself for the sake of her career.

Andrea felt genuine sympathy for her friend as Kim anxiously dabbed several layers of cream to the spot on her face. In the modeling business a single pound or a single pimple could easily cost a girl several assignments, which meant thousands of dollars. When her beauty was what a girl depended on for her living, it was all too easy to become obsessed with one's looks. Kim was just such a model, a woman-child who lived for the sole purpose of being beautiful. Andrea had tried in vain to interest her young friend first in art and then in archeology—anything.

The scent of nail polish remover filled the air as Kim settled herself on one of the double beds and began to do her nails. "Was he fast or something?" she asked, probing, wishing that Andy wasn't always so close-mouthed about her personal life.

"Hey, lay off," Andrea growled, growing annoyed, shaking the last of the stale chips into her palm. "I don't want to talk about him. In fact, I brought my bag because I'd like to stay here tonight. I'm afraid he might try to come up to my room and . . . I'd feel safer here."

Safer. The word lingered, reminding Kim of the delicious dangerousness about the man. Kim shot her friend a fascinated look that was both morbidly curious and frankly envious. "That fast?" she murmured, almost dreamily to herself, remembering the man's charismatic appeal, the sensual curve of those male lips, the breadth of muscled shoulders, the tall, lean length of him. Andy wasn't nearly as beautiful as she herself, nor as young, but Andy had the uncanny ability to attract the most interesting men . . . and keep them if she so chose, an ability that Kim sadly lacked.

Andrea deliberately ignored her, finding Kim's youthful illusions all but intolerable in her present mood. It was all too clear that Kim would have welcomed Race Jordan's attentions. If the poor child only knew. A man like that would gobble her as easily as the wolf ate Red Riding Hood's grandmother.

A vision of roguish male virility swirled in Andrea's imagination. Black twinkling eyes, eyes that knew too much where women were concerned. Fortunately, she herself was older, more mature, better able to see the man for what he was. And if she ever saw him again. . . . A strange, infuriating emotion rippled through her.

Andrea forced her thoughts from Race to Don. She felt suddenly anxious. She wanted to see Don so desperately. She *needed* to see him; but it was rapidly becoming obvious that it was going to be much more difficult than she'd originally thought when she'd made up her mind to take an assignment in Cancun just because he would be here.

Andrea cracked a peanut shell and then ate the two halves in silence, frown lines creasing her brow, her thoughts racing chaotically. It was nearly nine o'clock, and she'd decided against taking a cab to Don's rented villa. What good would that do? Several days ago, when she'd figured out the mansion's location, she'd hired a taxi and gone there even though she'd known Don wasn't due to arrive for two more days. She'd been dismayed by the sight of half a dozen men guarding the front of that tall white wall with the masses of purple bougainvillea spilling over it, dismayed as well by the wrought iron gate that was securely locked. She'd known the officials Don was visiting were important, but she hadn't anticipated quite this much security.

One of the difficulties Mexico presented was that, for almost nothing, one could hire a veritable army to guard a place. Getting inside the fortified compound was not going to be easy. At first she'd thought she could present herself to one of the guards and give them a note to take inside to Don. But now she feared the possibility that someone—inevitably she thought of a very specific and very irritating black-headed someone—would intercept any message from her to Don and give orders to prevent her entrance. She couldn't call because the villa's telephone number was unlisted.

Yesterday, she'd gone windsurfing and come up on the back side of the villa. The house was perched like a Mayan palace on a high coral cliff facing a strip of sugar-white beach and the turquoise sea. On three sides of the mansion the high wall with its splashy flowers and many guards surrounded the villa, but only a single guard patrolled the interior of the compound, which included the beach, the grounds and the winding drive.

Thus, her only chance of getting to Don seemed to be by boat, and since she was very experienced with boats, she didn't think that would be too difficult. She could easily tie one off at the end of the pier jutting into the protected lagoon, and slip ashore when the guard disappeared around the front of the house. If she went in the evening, it would be difficult for anyone from the house to spot a small unlit boat approaching on the darkening waves or see someone sprint lightly across the strip of beach. The incessant gurgle of the waves would mask both the sound of a motor and her quick steps across the thick sand. ·

Andrea frowned. Anxious though she was to see Don, she disliked the thought of having to sneak into his house as though she were a criminal. She had wanted to talk to him ever since Tuesday when that Buick had nearly struck her. She needed desperately to see him, to feel his gentle arms enfold her against his chest, his husky voice soothe away her fears. He was the one source of strength she felt she could turn to. Though she didn't know the exact hour his private plane would be landing in Cancun this evening, for days she'd counted on finding a way to see him tonight. But because of Race, everything seemed more complicated. She no longer felt she could simply go to the house and ask for him, and she was much too exhausted to arrange for a boat tonight. Thus she would simply have to wait until tomorrow evening; Don had told her when they'd last talked that he and the other diplomats would have scheduled activities during the day.

Suddenly she found herself wondering, not for the first time, why it was always so difficult for her to reach Don when she needed him. For the past four months he'd been the one who called her, but though he was eagerly attentive about doing so, there were times when that wasn't enough. There had been rare occasions when she'd had something so special to share with him that she hadn't thought she could wait for his call; but when she'd tried to reach him, she had never been able to. Oh, he'd given her his home telephone number, both in Texas and in Washington, but the trouble was he never answered when she called. Always, she got a recording. Of course, he would call back, but sometimes it took a few days. He would make excuses about why he was difficult to reach, that he'd been out of town, that he was involved in top secret negotiations he hadn't been able to interrupt. She had wanted to trust him so completely that she had never allowed herself to question the strangeness of the situation.

Before Don, she'd never been the sort of girl who wanted to sit around waiting for a man to have time for her, and she certainly wouldn't have gotten into this situation if what she had with Don weren't so special to her.

There had been no other man in her life since she'd met Don, and she'd realized only recently, although she hadn't told him, that she had fallen in love with him and was ready to make a commitment to him.

Though they had been dating four months and were both mature adults with physical needs, they had postponed sleeping together. On their first date Don had cupped her delicate chin in his large hand and gently kissed her goodnight in the darkened hall in front of her Village walk-up. Then, tenderly, he'd confided softly that he didn't want to rush sex between them, that she was so special that he wanted to develop a real relationship with her first. His shining eyes had held hers, cherishing her, and she'd known in that moment that she could grow to love this steady, dependable man. He was sincere and noble—so unlike the more physical and charming Enrico, so unlike every other man she'd known.

The men she'd dated since Enrico had demanded sex almost immediately, sometimes in very heated and unsavory ways, though she hadn't given in to them. She'd been so tired of wrestling matches that Don's approach had been a relief. Soon she found herself breaking dates with other men when he turned up in New York unexpectedly on weekends, and then she quit making the other dates at all.

Andrea was glad they'd taken the time to let their feelings deepen, but there came a time when a man and woman who loved inevitably needed more than friendship and kisses. She was achingly ready for more; long ago Enrico's hot embraces had awakened in her a woman's desires, and she'd lived too long without satisfying them. Tomorrow night she would tell Don that she loved him, and she hoped with all her heart that he was ready to let her show him how much.

The matter seemed suddenly urgent. She couldn't stop herself from remembering this afternoon and her shockingly hot response to Race Jordan, a man who was little more than an odious stranger to her. Even now, as she thought of him, she could almost feel the blaze of warmth that his mere touch had sent quivering through her, the fevered sensation in her body when his masculine, rock-hard thighs pressed tightly to her, the warmth of his skin beneath her fingertips, the musky scent of him. She'd been too aware of him then, just as she was now. Why couldn't she rid her thoughts of the man? It made her feel unfaithful to Don. At last, she reassured herself with the thought that the only reason she was so vulnerable to this stranger she actually disliked was because she was a passionate woman who'd been too long without a man. She consoled herself with the thought that once Don made her his she would completely forget Race.

Later, as she snuggled sleepily beneath the crisp sheets of Kim's extra bed, she was still thinking of Don, trying to frame the exact phrases she would use to express her love to him tomorrow night.

After that pleasant task was completed she made her battle plans for the next day. She was through with her part of the photographic shooting and would have the whole day free. It was imperative that she disappear lest Race find her. Clearly she couldn't stay in the *zona hoteles*.

She browsed through several guidebooks trying to determine what she could do to avoid Race. At last she decided to take an all-day tour to Tulum, a splendid Mayan archeological site perched on the edge of the turquoise Caribbean, with the world's second-longest barrier reef in full view, white froth breaking over it. Near Tulum was Xel-Ha, a natural aquarium she read about where she planned to view first-hand the extraordinary array of vividly colored fish. She could take along her snorkeling gear and spend some of her time swimming. Yes, she would have a delightful day, marveling at the archeological wonders of the Mayans, swimming, and lunching at the expensive restaurant at Akumal, the beach there being something out of a James Bond movie. Race could spend his day searching for her for all she cared. At the thought of his frustration, a tiny smile formed at the corners of her lips.

Flame-red tresses splayed vividly against her pillow as she placed her head into its softness and stared dreamily up at the rough texture of the ceiling.

Tonight she felt strangely aroused, her womanly needs stronger than usual. She told herself the reason for this was because she knew she would soon be seeing Don. For an instant the treacherous image of Race recurred, and a disturbing wave of heat surged inside her. Angrily she snapped her eyes shut against a vision of dark male virility that made her ache with desire. The moment her lashes lay still against the paleness of her face, she was asleep; her mind, even in sleep, remained turbulently awhirl. For her, dreams were filled not with Don and the special sweetness of their love but of a bold dark pirate who was tall and handsome, a giant of a man with flashing black eyes and lips that curled with sardonic amusement. He had swept her up in arms so hard they seemed living stone, against his body that burned with driving male need: yet when he kissed her, he did so with lips so infinitely soft they explored the depths of her soul.

And in her sleep his name escaped her lips in the gentlest moan of surrender.

Chapter 3

RISING ABOVE THE PASSIONATELY POIGNANT SPANISH LYR-
ics and the dozen strumming guitars of a band of
mariachis were the swell of laughter and the mingle of
voices speaking earnestly in two languages. The villa
was brilliantly lit and, viewed from the aqua lagoon,
seemed to pulse with life.

The party inside the house was elaborate even for
Mexican diplomatic affairs. Servants carrying silver
trays bustled between the important guests, serving
drinks and delectable *hors d'oeuvres*. Tables draped in
white linen were piled high with food, the scent of spicy
hot Spanish dishes wafting in the air. There was
seafood of all varieties—broiled lobsters that glistened
the rosiest of reds, oysters, scallops, shrimp *paté*,
marinated salmon in tarragon. The list was endless.
The food, divine.

The men in their dark conservative suits were a

mixture of wealthy businessmen, government officials, and American diplomats. Their women were beautiful pampered creatures who cared little for political talk. They were smothered in gold and jewels, swishing gracefully about in their flowing designer gowns studded with hand-sewn bugle beads, eyeing one another with vague traces of envy.

Despite the attractions of the lavish *fiesta* as well as a certain specific feminine attraction who had the softly voluptuous dimensions Race admired in a woman and great, glowing velvet-dark eyes that seemed to seek his every time his glance chanced upon her, Race had shunned the party. He'd been damnably irritable the past two days; he was not in the mood for a party. Besides, he reasoned, Don was the politician, not Race.

Race stood outside the mansion, alone on one of the vast stone terraces overlooking the crashing breakers of the Caribbean on one side and the lagoon on the other. He felt oddly restless, not himself at all, and from time to time he paced the length of the rock walkway, his black varnished shoes resounding. A strong breeze gusted up from the sea, waving the oleander so its pink blossoms brushed the house, ruffling the palm fronds, the wind touching everything with its sultry humidity and sting of salt. A full moon hung low on the horizon, creating a silver path across the waves.

Race paused, leaning heavily on his elbows against the low white wall that edged the terrace, his swift gaze scanning the water. For an instant he thought he saw something dark flicker on the glistening waves. But whatever it was dipped beneath the curl of the surf, and he saw nothing of interest other than a gull swooping low above the waves.

His attention shifted to his magnificent white motor yacht, *The Jordana*. Two years ago he'd had her custom-built in Florida so he could fly from his ranch in the Texas hill country to Galveston and cruise the Gulf of Mexico in comfort. The chop was high enough, even in the lagoon, so that she rode uneasily against her dock lines, but Race was not worried. He had checked her earlier and knew she was secure. Besides, Felix, the wizened Mexican-American he'd hired two years ago to care for the yacht along with Jake Jordan, his college-age nephew, were both on board.

As Race continued to gaze toward *The Jordana,* his real concentration was on a certain red-headed model who'd plagued his thoughts ever since two nights ago, when she'd disappeared from Chichén Itzá in his car. He didn't like being thwarted by anyone, and she'd done more than thwart him. She'd put him to an unconscionable amount of trouble.

Without amusement he remembered the agony of the four-hour ride in a third class bus from Chichén Itzá to the city limits of Cancun, where he'd jumped off at the first bus stop to hail a cab. As if jolting down the road in that sardine-can rattle trap that stopped for additional passengers at every clump of gum trees along the highway wasn't enough, he'd been squashed between a querulous fat man with oiled black hair, who reeked of garlic and other odors Race didn't even attempt to define, and several cages of equally foul-smelling chickens. No use throwing open a window, because then the bus filled nauseatingly with diesel fumes. When the three brown-faced students in front of him had leaned over their tattered seat to leer at him, and discovered he was not only an American, and thus a capitalist, but that he could speak Spanish, his fate was sealed. Their eyes began to gleam with fervor, and they began spouting their communistic philosophies with the fierce enthusiasm of zealots who wouldn't have tired of their diatribe if the trip had lasted four days, never mind four hours. Everyone on the bus eventually joined in the debate and all were shouting their last points when the *gringo* stumbled from the bus to the curb, weak with a mixture of relief and exhaustion. But, for all its faults (and for an American used to his physical comforts there had been many), the bus had been the only certain means of transportation back to Cancun that night.

One thought had sustained him—the vision of that redheaded she-devil safely in the clutches of the Mexican police, where she could trouble Don no further.

But again she'd thwarted him. No sooner had he called the police than he'd discovered that the *señorita* with the hair of fire was still one step ahead of him. She had obligingly returned his rental car and deliberately stuck him for a week's rent. It had taken two hours of polite, and then not-so-polite cajoling in Spanish to unravel that mess. In the end, he'd had to take the car for a week.

He'd spent all day in the car searching for her, but she'd vanished as utterly as though she'd melted into the sea. When he'd questioned Stefano, the man had looked up impatiently from his camera and viewed him through narrowed, suspicious eyes, telling him nothing. The little blonde model who had smiled so charmingly at him the day before had remained guardedly frozen, staring at herself in her vanity, as though silenced by her friend of whom she was obviously very much in awe. Race grudgingly admired Andrea's ability to inspire loyalty, whatever her methods, because no amount of charm or enticement had affected them. Finally he'd grown so exasperated he'd given up. Nor was she in her hotel room—he'd bribed a maid to open it.

The question was: where was she? And was she foolhardy enough to try to see Don? As Race remembered the brilliant fire in those green eyes and the way she'd thrust out her dainty jaw so stubbornly at him, he was afraid the answer to that question was yes.

Damn the woman. Where the hell was she?

"*¿Señor?* Do you like a drink?" The softest and most charmingly accented of voices interrupted his thoughts. He whirled, his black eyes alive with sardonic interest as they met the velvet eyes of the beautiful woman he'd admired earlier. His male gaze drifted to her uplifted breasts daringly exposed above tight black satin. Strangely, despite her stunning beauty and the invitation he read in her dark eyes, he felt no desire. But then maybe it wasn't so strange. He'd never liked being chased by a woman, no matter how attractive she was.

"Thank you," he murmured, taking the drink from her hands, noting cynically how they lingered too long upon his. It was strong tequila, and it burned his throat as he bolted a draught. He looked down his long, straight nose at her. He didn't want to be alone with her. His bronzed hand slid caressingly to her waist, and he said, "Why don't we go back inside and dance?"

She was disappointed but she acquiesced, placing her hand on his arm with gentle possessiveness. As Race turned to lead her toward the door, a shadow flitted lightly across the silver beach, disappearing into the thick shadow of the palms, but he was aware of nothing except the girl on his arm and his vague feeling of annoyance at being trapped into a flirtation he hadn't sought.

Race drew the girl tightly into the circle of his arms, and even before they began dancing he was conscious of her dreamily provocative gaze, of her soft body brushing his. Exactly why he remained so unaffected by her was a puzzle he was too indifferent to ponder. Vaguely he wondered if his lack of response was the first sign that he was getting older.

They began dancing to several melodic Spanish love

songs, and Race was aware of himself constantly scanning the crowd of faces for the one he sought. Then he would remember the guards outside and his orders to them, and force himself to relax and turn his attention back to his beautiful partner. There was no way the strong-minded Miss Ford could get inside the compound, no matter how she might try, he reassured himself.

The music stopped, and Race glanced past the band to determine why. His black gaze rivetted to the stunning couple who'd just arrived, and his hands fell abruptly away from the waist of the soft, feminine body in his arms. He stared in amazement at the handsome couple who'd just arrived. A tall silver–haired man strode into the room, leading a woman with hair the color of bright flame.

Beneath his dark tan, Race went white, and his fingers clinched around the dainty wrist he held.

It was the American ambassador to Mexico making his entrance with his usual fanfare, and on his arm was Andrea. The ambassador's entourage swarmed excitedly behind him, but the man himself had eyes only for the exquisite woman at his side. And she *was* exquisite, Race conceded, for so tall a woman. Oddly, the mere sight of her affected him in a way the more beautiful woman beside him could not. A strange, hot emotion surged through him.

Andrea was as different from the other women in the room as a wildflower from an artificially nutured orchid. Her red hair spilled over her slim white shoulders in wild disarray as though tousled by a strong sea breeze. She wore a shimmering silk Halston, her gown of flowing jade-green chiffon that clung to her figure as though damp, its simple style accentuating not only the extreme height and slimness of her body but its flowing grace as well. There was a glowing naturalness about her, a loveliness of the spirit that owed nothing to artifice. Not a single jewel glimmered against her pale skin. It was she herself who dazzled.

Despite her height, her every movement was dainty and feather-light, and to Race she seemed vulnerable and small, and far too attractive. He remembered how feminine and responsive she'd been when he'd held her that once in his encircling arms. He was uncomfortably conscious that his every sense was attuned to her.

Even from across the room, Race could distinguish the velvety sound of her laughter from all the other sounds in the room. He was hauntingly aware of it, of the warm pleasantness of its rippling softness, of a strange desire to be the man who caused it. He was aware too of the way her long fingers were clenched around the ambassador's arm as though he were a giant shield and she Joan of Arc ready to do battle.

"How in the hell did she . . . ?" Only when the dark beauty at his side glanced questioningly up at him did Race realize he had spoken aloud. For a brief moment his sense of humor prevailed despite the gravity of the situation, and he couldn't help muttering to himself in grudging admiration, "I'll give her one thing—she certainly knows how to arrive in style." Then a dark fury began to burn through him at the brazen irresponsibility of her action, and he knew he had to suppress his own passion for her, as well as his anger, and find a way to stop her from seeing Don . . . and avert what could only be a disaster.

He stepped more deeply into the shadows at the edge of the dance floor to observe Andrea while he thought. Her green eyes were wide, the only indication of her extreme nervousness, he decided, as she searched the room—for Don. Thankfully, Don and Linda were still conferring with the Mexican oil producers and bankers down at the poolside guest house. But Race knew he didn't have much time, since the meeting would be over soon.

Andrea was moving easily among the guests, and she seemed to know quite a few of the Americans. Race was reminded of the fact that she was an international celebrity, that in New York she must grace parties and functions where other such celebrities mingled. She had obviously met Don in that manner.

He watched the diaphanous gown swirl around her body, clinging to her, revealing her curves as though it were a transparent veil. Blood rushed through his veins, as well as a hot jealousy that other men were also looking at her.

The Mexican men were even more enchanted with her than the Americans who knew her: to them, a woman of her stature and hair coloring was an exotically flamboyant creature. They vied to meet her, scrambling to clutch her hands and kiss them. For some reason it angered Race to watch them paw her as she smiled and laughed, attempting her atrocious Spanish which they found so charming.

Race forced himself to suppress the unwanted emotions he felt for her and only partially succeeded. Every time he looked at her he forgot she was his enemy, and he found himself thinking only of her allure as a woman. His bold gaze swept her again before he tore his eyes away.

Damn the party and the woman's superb sense of timing! Race thought violently. On any other night he could have easily evicted her, but the last thing he wanted was a scene. No telling what Andrea would do or say if he tried to throw her out; things seemed to get out of hand rather quickly between the two of them.

Race couldn't stand idly by a moment longer. Nodding a curt dismissal to his dancing partner, he charged toward Andrea.

Andrea saw him the minute he moved. He was, after all, the tallest and most charismatic man in the room. His bold, ravishing look descended from her breasts to her hips and she flushed. Too well she remembered the thrill of his touch at the ballcourt, and she inwardly quivered at the memory of his hard body holding her close.

Her eyes lifted to his face, and the mere sight of his roughly sculpted profile instantly disrupted the evenness of her breathing. He was so damnably, so breathlessly good-looking. She shrank against the ambassador, her hand involuntarily going to her throat to cover its fluttering pulse. For a moment she was more afraid of her own feelings than she was of him. Then she reminded herself that he'd tried to abduct her, that he was no handsome innocent.

As Race swept through the crowd toward her, a savage dark wind mowing a path through a wheat field, the color drained from her face. Against her vivid hair her skin took on the grayish pallor of a person who was severely ill. Then her heart began to thud with wild rapidity.

She knew that he approached for only one purpose: to prevent her from seeing Don.

"Good evening, Mr. Ambassador," Race said courteously to the ambassador, his brilliant black gaze seeing only the pale shaking woman at the diplomat's side. He wished he were glad she was so obviously afraid of him, but for some incomprehensible reason he took no pleasure in the complacent notion that perhaps she wouldn't be as difficult to manage as he'd first thought. He was aware only of her softness, her femininity, and of a surge of male protectiveness mingling with his desire.

"Good to see you, Race. Do you know Miss Andrea F——?"

"We've met," came the steely reply he had to force, and though Andrea didn't look up she could feel his hot, male gaze sweep over her like a molten physical caress. "In fact I want to personally thank you for bringing her," Race continued silkily. "I've been trying to get in touch with Andy the past couple of days."

"Andy?" The sound of his velvet voice tingled like fire. The use of her nickname suggested an intimacy that caught her off guard. She felt hot, then cold. Suddenly she was furious that she was such a weak-minded female where this charismatic abductor-womanizer was concerned. How did *he* know her nickname? How dare he use it? Andrea fumed, her sensuous response lessening and her fear abating as her willingness to fight this impossible man rallied.

"We only happened to bump into each other in the garden," the ambassador admitted.

"How fortunate. . . ." Race murmured, soft irony coating his deep voice. His black eyes locked with Andrea's for an instant, and it was as though an electric current charged through them both.

"But Andrea and I are old acquaintances," the ambassador said, smiling affectionately down at her. "I first got to know Andy two years ago backstage at the Met. She was dating a certain rather flamboyant tenor. Later we went to Sardi's, and I don't remember when I've had more fun with anyone."

"Really? You have the advantage over me then," Race replied smoothly, leashing the emotion that pounded through him. "We've only just met, the other day at Chichén Itzá. But it was . . . quite a memorable occasion." His white smile flashed. Andrea glared militantly up at him as he continued, even as she recalled the molten embrace of his body, the devastating impact of his maleness. "We share many common interests, and as I told her then, I'm looking forward to getting to know her better." Deliberately he inserted a husky note in the last and allowed his hard eyes to soften as they met hers that had narrowed.

Andrea rasped, "You are mistaken, sir. We have nothing in common, and I haven't the slightest desire to further an acquaintance with you." Why then was she trembling from his nearness? Why was she breathless when he looked at her?

Fortunately the ambassador was distracted by a Mexican general and had turned away to speak to him.

"Then it is up to me to show you just how wrong you are," Race said evenly, still smiling the false white smile of his that she found maddening because it accentuated his dark good looks. He effortlessly unpeeled her stiff fingers from the ambassador's sleeve. She was aware of the fire of his touch; she felt it in every pulsating fiber of her body.

He did not touch her roughly, but with a casual mastery that left her feeling like his helpless captive. Andrea considered his action as well as her own treacherous response with horror, but she could scarcely fight him physically like some bawd in a barroom, though it took all her will power not to. The people in this room were important personages whose esteem was important to Don.

Strong, warm hands trapped her to that hard body, that vitally male physique laced with tough muscle that she hadn't been able to delete from her consciousness since he'd first touched her. She was disgustingly aware of the strange heat bubbling in her arteries as he held her tightly against his length.

"Let me go!" she hissed through white, compressed lips. "Or. . . ."

"Or what?" he prompted, forcing her further away from the ambassador's protection.

"Or I'll scream!" It was only a crazy bluff, but Race didn't know that. He felt the softness of her breasts pressing against his chest; he caught the dizzying fragrance of her delicate perfume. Hot blood surged through his veins, improbably fierce and turbulent.

She opened her mouth as though to scream. Like hell! he thought, so infuriated with this impossible woman that he forgot his desire to avoid a scene and brought his mouth down hard toward hers.

Frantically, her hands, their fingers splayed widely apart, pushed ineffectually against his chest. But it was no use. She was aware of his sharply indrawn breath before his lips touched hers. Then she could only gaze helplessly as his dark face blurred and his mouth crushed down upon hers.

His arm curved around her slim waist and hauled her so tightly against his body that she felt the imprint of every male part of him from the hard flatness of his stomach to the long columns of his thighs.

His lips ravaged hers, and she caught the flavor of tequila on his breath as she tried to twist away. He forced her lips open to accept the intimacy of his tongue. He kissed her long and insolently, invading her mouth, thrusting warmly into its velvet dampness: he found the taste of her delicious.

He noted that her smooth skin was lightly crusted with salt, her gown wet with sea spray. He knew then how she had come, but he was past caring. In a haze of desire he held her against his body, plundering her soft shaking lips with a savagery that until this moment had been alien to him.

Andrea felt giddy, yet wildly alive. Her response only served to enrage her further.

This couldn't be happening. He was a madman. A brute. Don . . . ? The slow heat of Race's arousing kiss was destroying her will to oppose him. She felt the heat of his long body against hers, the violent thunder of his heart against her breasts. In a frenzy she tried to twist from his strong grasp, but her long hair, that was tangled in his arms and hands, was so cruelly yanked by her efforts that tears sprang to her eyes.

"Stop fighting me," he growled savagely. "Or it'll be even worse."

No man threatened her. She thrashed even more wildly in his powerful embrace, and suddenly to her horror she felt herself being swung off balance and lifted into his strong arms as easily as though she weighed no more than a child.

Race was aware that people had turned to observe their passionate exchange with avid interest.

"You asked for it!" he muttered thickly against Andrea's quivering lips. She stared at him with open-mouthed shock as he forced a jaunty smile and raised his husky voice to the stunned crowd observing them, his black eyes flashing with amusement. "Gentlemen, ladies . . . excuse us please. A lover's quarrel that can only be mended in privacy."

He spoke in Spanish. She did not know what else he said, only that everyone laughed.

"A lovers' quarrel." She went hot all over with the most intense shame she'd ever felt. How could he? They would think her no better than some common little thing he'd picked up for a night's amusement. How dared he make a fool of her? She wanted to slap him, to claw his dark face for that glib lie, and the knowing laughter that had followed it. When she kicked out and would have protested, his lips closed brutally over hers once more. As he strode from the room, she heard the humiliating bursts of scattered applause and shouted male bravos.

Things like this didn't happen at elegant political cocktail parties in the twentieth century, her mind stormed. He was carrying her up a swirling spiral of stairs to the bedrooms as though he were a caveman bringing home a rare catch. For one of the first times in her life she felt herself overwhelmed by a man far more powerful than she, and she was at a loss to know what she should do.

Only when they reached the darkened landing did he set her down, drawing her into the shadows, holding her still in his tight embrace, arching her slim body over his arm so that her hips fitted his provocatively. He was shaking as though he were in the grip of an over-powering emotion, and his breaths came in harsh gasps.

A raging force, an emotion long-denied that was stronger than fury, drove him, as his hands moved over her, roughly caressing her breasts. Then he bent his head to hers and kissed her with a passion no man had ever kissed her with before. They were both consumed with the wild, hot, blinding fury of it, and she could only cling to him for support in a bewildering world that was swirling with tumultuous passions. The heat of his mouth evoked feelings she'd never felt before, and a wild electricity traced thrillingly through her.

Skilled hands roved over her body. His lips followed, caressing each tenderly inflamed part of her. He cupped her small breasts and lowered his mouth to kiss them through the gauzy green material until they peaked rigidly against the dampened fabric molding itself to their swollen shape. Then he brought his mouth to her lips once more, and kissed them with a fierce male hunger that sent waves of pleasure pulsating through her trembling body. She was his, and he was hers in this time of madness.

She was lost in a world of desire; she was fevered with an aching need that, until this moment had been unknown to her. In the dark silence she heard his deep voice muttering unintelligible lovewords between his bruising kisses. A part of her wanted him to go on kissing her and making wanton promises forever, so she stirred queerly with disappointment when his hot mouth drew away, hovering inches from hers, the warmth of his irregular breaths tickling her sensitive skin.

Very gently his roughened hand reached up and caressed the smoothness of her cheek in wonder. She was startled by his unexpected gentleness, and when she shyly ventured a glance at him, she saw that his dark face was gravely tender. His caressing fingers were doing odd things in the pit of her belly, and the wanton need to feel his hands roam just that tenderly over her naked body, to explore her intimately, flared in her. Somehow this new tenderness in him as well as in herself was more deeply threatening than the violence of his passion.

At last he released her, and drew his hand away, his black, intense eyes holding hers, searing her as hotly as the fire of his kisses, touching her as gently as the light grazing of his warm fingertips. For a timeless moment she felt drawn to him, and a strange, soft tide of feeling swept over her.

This couldn't be. She couldn't desire this man when she loved another. There was no commitment, no love, nothing; and yet that was wrong too. Her feelings for this man were stronger than anything ever before in her life. Suddenly Don seemed as vague as a ghostly apparition, while Race's presence pounded through her body like a hot, volatile drumbeat. What was happening to her? But he gave her no time to ponder this question. He lifted her into his arms and carried her down the hall.

Vaguely she was aware of the lavishness of the suite he carried her into, of the massive double doors to his bedroom, of the vast bed with its scarlet velvet bedcovers neatly turned down for the night, of the enormous bath with marble and gilt fixtures beyond.

Just being alone with him in the privacy of this room increased the intimate bond between them. In one corner stood a covered easel, and she caught the faint scent of turpentine and paint. A vague curiosity stirred within her, but she was too passionately involved with Race to pursue it.

He was standing, holding her at the edge of the large bed, when he gently released her. They stood facing one another, their bodies touching, the tips of her breasts against his chest, their lower bodies comfortably nestled, while his slowly moving hands deliberately lingered on her waist and shoulder as he savored the splendor of touching her, of learning her. The pulse in her throat fluttered beneath his expert fingers as he began to explore her body, moving his palm lower beneath her thick hair to caress the nape of her neck. His other hand caught the zipper at the back of her dress and drew it downward. She could feel his hand moving against her bare flesh.

Her own trembling fingers were fumbling with the buttons of his shirt and then sliding across the warm bronze flesh, marveling at the smooth muscle lightly covered with dark hairs.

"W-what are we doing?" she heard herself ask in wonder. It was like a dream. This wasn't happening to her. This was but the sensuous figment of her imagination, and yet at the same time it was all too gloriously real. She was hot and alive and breathless. Her body was moist and ready as he held her closely against the swollen pressure of his loins.

"Mmmmm." His husky murmur was the only indication that he heard her. His sensual mouth had lowered to inflame the sensitive skin above her breasts. He was pushing aside the neckline of her gown so his lips would have provocative access to the soft mounds of flesh thrusting beneath his tongue.

"This is so crazy. . . ." She gasped, choking off her utterance, as his mouth closed over her nipple and he began to suck. Tiny, thrilling spasms traced through her as his lips nibbled, plucked, and sucked at the roseate bud of her flesh.

"Let me go." The words were ironic. She heard the throb of desire in her voice as her body melted against him. "Please . . . ?" But as she swayed to him, her hands tightly gripping his waist, it seemed instead that she was begging him to take her.

Indeed, physically, she made no attempt to resist him. Her breasts swelled under the onslaught of his flaming kisses. Lowering her head, Andrea went in search of those lips that were setting her aflame. A searing fire stung her arteries when she found his mouth and surrendered to their male domination. His hands curved around her slender back, gathering her close, crushing her breasts against his bared chest.

He was lowering her to the bed when several sharp knocks resounded through the room. For an instant Andrea thought it was merely the mad hammering of her own heartbeats. But then she heard a woman's voice softly calling Race's name.

Race lifted his head, his expression reluctant, his gaze burning hungrily over Andrea. "What the hell?" He suppressed the rest of the oath.

"She wants you," Andrea said. "You'd better go before she figures out a way to get in here and finds us like this."

"I'll be right back. Don't go away." He was smiling as his black eyes feasted on her sexual dishevelment, on the pouting pleasure-peaks of her breasts, bobbing from her ragged breathing. Her gown was pooled at her knees, all her womanly treasures wantonly displayed for his enjoyment.

He was buttoning his shirt and smoothing back his hair as he strode from the bedroom. For a moment Andrea lay still, wrapped in the sensual mood he had aroused.

But as she listened to the faint murmur of his voice mingling with the girl's, she began to grow restless. It was doubtless the beautiful girl he had been dancing with earlier, and she had come to his room seeking him.

Andrea sat up in bed, feeling suddenly cold. She reached for her dress and pulled it back on. She heard Race's deep chuckle before the door closed and the lock clicked securely. His footsteps were heavy as they fell on the glossy stretches of white marble between the thick Indian throw rugs.

He was returning to seduce her. The very man who'd tried to abduct her. The very man who opposed her relationship with Don. She was crazy to have let things get so out of hand between them.

By the time Race reached the room she no longer felt so much in his power. Into her confused brain cold sanity was slowly returning.

Weakly, she noted he was unbuttoning his shirt again, exposing a strip of teak flesh. As she looked up into his expectant black eyes, she scorned herself for her addle-brained behavior, realizing with horror that the man whose caresses had so thoroughly aroused her was a man she surely despised. The vibrant *mariachi* music and the revelry beneath drifted to her ears, and she remembered how he'd recently humiliated her downstairs. And this last was surely the ultimate humiliation.

Rage and hate and shame flowed back into her as she stiffened with intense emotion. She stood up as he neared the bed, and when he attempted to take her in his arms and resume the sensual feast he had had to leave, she reached up and cracked her palm against his face.

"How dare you . . . ?" she muttered, but her voice was thin.

He stood perfectly still as two ruddy marks flamed

against the swarthy skin of his cheek. His eyes were fierce.

"You have no more decency than a barbarian or a pirate—carrying me off to . . . to . . ." She sputtered to a halt, feeling so utterly confused she couldn't go on. It wasn't as though she'd been an unwilling partner—but that fact galled her more than any other. She felt remorse that she'd struck him, and a lingering tenderness toward him despite her anger. Blast the man. She didn't know how she felt anymore.

"Then we make a fine pair," he muttered, "the way you chase after my brother like a cheap tramp, and then kiss me and invite me into bed like you haven't had a man in . . ." All the while, his hot eyes drifted over her body, and her skin felt as if he'd burned her.

The contempt in his gaze as well as the sneer in his dark tone stung, and she winced as though he'd struck her.

"Don't say it!" she managed. Did he think she wanted to respond to him like that? Even now she was keenly conscious of his bronzed body, of his overpowering virility, of her own body trembling in awareness of his.

Don's brother. Her mind reeled as this fact sank in. This jeering, passionate, violent man, this man whose mere touch could make her weak with desire, whose caress could soften her heart, was Don's brother.

"B-but that's impossible. You don't have the same last names! You don't look like each other at all!" she blurted.

"Don looks like his father, and I look like mine," Race explained succinctly. "My mother divorced my father to marry Don's."

Andrea stared blankly. She went cold, then hot, as this new and terrible reality sank in. Race was telling her the truth. She could see it in his eyes, in the hardness of his strong features. Had she known, she would have behaved differently. She would have been friendly from the first. She would never have driven off in his car and left him to find his own way back to Cancun. And she would have somehow managed to suppress the heated response his kisses had evoked.

But she hadn't known. As she scanned the tanned skin stretched over chiseled, masculine features, she realized she couldn't have guessed. Never were two men more different. Don with his golden hair, the softness of his eyes, the gentleness of his nature, his sexual nobility, his seriousness toward his altruistic mission in life. He was a public servant determined to use his high office to help others. While Race . . . She realized suddenly that despite her intimate feelings toward him, she knew absolutely nothing about the kind of man he was.

Odd—she felt she'd known him always. Of one thing she was sure: he was not nearly as sexually noble as his brother, but neither was he the odious monster she'd tried to pretend he was.

"You're wrong about me," she said stiffly, "just as I've been wrong about you. I'm no tramp. I love Don."

"You have a strange way of behaving toward me for a woman so deeply in love," he said cynically. His eyes boldly traveled over her from the brilliant hair that spilled in glorious tangles about her shoulders down over the slender body that the warm light washed with golden tones. She was a prize he'd almost won, and in that moment, her alluring nearness made his failure to bed her (which was causing him acute physical discomfort) all the more painful. He felt she'd teased him into this state of deep and fermenting male hunger that she would not appease.

"I . . . I . . . am at a loss to explain myself. I should never have come up here . . . or given you the impression . . . I didn't know what I was doing. It was just something that happened." She was twisting her hands as she stared steadfastly at the floor.

Suddenly she felt his rough palm cup her delicate chin, and his touch was like a flashfire setting her entire body ablaze. Slowly he raised her face, and though she couldn't meet the intensity of his eyes, she was aware of them searching her features.

"I wanted you, Race. I can't deny it," she whispered. "Nothing like tonight has ever happened to me before."

His expression, though no longer angry, was frankly skeptical.

She flushed. "I'm sorry if I led you on tonight. It wasn't intentional. And I . . . I suppose I should apologize for the way I acted toward you the first time we met," she went on with quiet earnestness. "If you'd only told me who you were, I would never have driven off in your car and left you at Chichén Itzá. You see, I was afraid of you. I know how ridiculous that sounds now, but I was."

He seemed so hard and so tense to her. She smiled disarmingly at him.

Race felt himself softening. Humility—from her—was something he was unprepared to deal with.

"Please, Race, try to understand. I didn't know who you were!"

Vivid green eyes seemed to pierce his soul with their intense supplication.

Race's thoughts whirled uneasily. Perhaps he had come on too strong the other day, but he'd been so determined to stop her from seeing Don. Suddenly Race wasn't thinking of Don, but of Andrea, and of the way she affected him. What was it about her that made her so damnably attractive at moments like this? He had never liked the combination of red hair and freckles, and she was much too tall and thin for his taste. Still, there was something about the sparkle of those green eyes that made her seem so vitally, so irresistibly alive, and the soft curve of her lips made her seem gentle and feminine, even alluring. It was simply the force of her personality that compelled him, he decided.

"You were gone before I had a chance to tell you," he admitted grudgingly, not liking to think that this woman, his brother's woman, had a power over him that no woman since Carolyn had had. For no reason at all he thought of Rebecca at home in Texas and the unspoken understanding between them, and for the first time he felt shackled by a commitment that had always seemed so right until this moment.

"I have a tendency to fly off the handle sometimes," Andrea conceded sweetly.

"Don't you think that's putting things a little mildly?" Race queried, a smile in his deep baritone.

"I hope I didn't inconvenience you too much," she said, genuine concern in her soft voice, "when I took your car."

"Uh . . . no," he said slowly, considering his words. "My trip back was . . . very educational. I learned a great deal about the Mexican people and . . . er . . . Mexican politics." So much more than he had wanted to learn, he thought ruefully, about two subjects that had never interested him in the slightest.

"I'm so glad." She smiled up at him, acutely relieved, and the brilliance of her eyes and the sweetness of her expression unexpectedly caught at his heart. She reddened suddenly with new shame and remorse and gasped, "But . . . what about the rental agency? I deliberately charged you for a week's rental . . . you must think I'm simply awful!"

"I straightened that out. It gave me a chance to

practice my Spanish," he said easily, dismissing the two-hour battle with a wave of his hand as well as the fact that he now had a car on his hands he didn't need.

"I really do feel awful about what I did . . . now that I know you're Don's brother. I . . . I do want Don's family to accept me."

Accept her. Her words brought Race sharply back to the matter at hand. There was no way they would accept her. Too much was at stake. Her relationship with Don had to be dealt with at once.

"I need to talk to you," he said, his voice hardening, "about Don."

His gravity alarmed her. "He's not . . . ill, is he?" she asked, fear in her voice.

"No."

Gently, he caught her elbow, and guided her into the outer room. He flipped the lightswitch, flooding the room with light. Through the massive double doors she could still see his bedroom. The vast bed with its bedcovers were messily tumbled, a reminder of their passion. She fought to suppress a blush as she remembered his embraces and her own too ardent responses.

She was too aware of him as a man even now, of his tanned maleness, of the sexual charisma he exuded. Just being alone with him made her want him in a way she had no right to want him, especially now that she knew who he was.

Race beckoned her to sit on the sofa while he strode across the room to the bar. He was splashing golden *Chivas* over ice into a crystal glass.

"Care to join me?" He lifted the squatty bottle toward her in invitation. She thought his dark expression more cynical than usual.

Though her throat was dry, she shook her head. Liquor was the last thing she needed.

His long strides carried him back to her side, and he

eased himself onto the thick cushions beside her, angling his great body so that he faced her, his knee brushing hers accidentally. Or not so accidentally. She couldn't be sure, for he smiled sardonically when she jumped away, flushing brightly.

There was too much knowledge in his smile and in his eyes, she thought uneasily. When she tried to back away from his disturbing nearness, she found herself imprisoned between the arm of the couch and Race's muscled body. She stared up at him uncomfortably. He swirled his drink so that the ice cubes tinkled, and then drained the glass in a single draught as though he needed the drink for courage.

"There's no reason to be afraid of me just because we . . ." He let his deep voice trail off suggestively as his gaze slid past her to the bedroom doors.

"I'm not afraid."

"You're trembling."

"But I'm not afraid." No, it was not fear that made her tremble, but her desire for him.

"Good." He let the matter drop, and for a while they sat in silence.

She found herself studying the male perfection of his features—the darkness of his skin that covered his angular bone structure, the thickness of his brows over his beautiful black eyes. His lashes were so long and dense and curled that every model she knew would have sold her soul to possess them. His sensual lips . . . her gaze lingered on his mouth, helplessly remembering the deliciously wanton sensation of his kisses, his mouth on her nipples, his hard body pressing potently against her. She crimsoned at the memory, and with an effort looked wildly away, trying to focus on a vase of enormous, brightly colored Mexican flowers. It was suddenly very difficult to regulate her breathing.

"What did you want to tell me about Don?" she asked falteringly.

"I don't know how much Don has told you," he began gently, a vague grimness in his soft tone, "about himself."

Uneasily Andrea was reminded of how little she really knew about Don. Don had always drawn her out and listened to her talk about herself without sharing confidences of his own with her. At first this had been a welcome relief after Enrico's egotistical selfishness, but after a while she'd longed to know more about Don. But even when she'd asked, he'd skillfully evaded her questions. She'd frequently teased him that being in politics had taught him how to avoid questions he didn't want to answer. He'd laughed, but he'd told her nothing except the same trivia she already knew.

"I know that he really wanted to be an artist, but that he lacked the talent to follow that career," she said softly, her face aglow as she spoke of Don.

"Don says that to everyone," Race said coolly. "But the truth of the matter is that he's a born politician. When he was six he'd go out to our barn and make political speeches to the horses. By the time he was ten, he . . ."

"I met him in the Metropolitan Museum of Fine Art," she declared defensively, "at an exhibition of magic realistic and surrealistic art."

Race studied her face in surprise. "That figures," he said, and somehow it did.

"Our interest in art was what drew us together at first."

"And then later?" Race was aware that he was suddenly unhealthily interested in the exact nature of their relationship. The thought of her slim white body laced intimately in his brother's was distasteful to him.

"He's so different from the other men I had known. So noble," she tried to explain. "I came to respect him. To love him."

Race looked more cynical than ever. "But he never told you about me?"

"No."

"Did you know that the co-op on Park Avenue where he sometimes took you belonged to me?"

"No."

"When I came to New York I found the note you left for him."

So that was how Race had known about her relationship with Don. Don hadn't told his brother himself. Why? Why hadn't he? Why *couldn't* he? Something in Race's manner, a new softness, his very kindliness terrified her: she sensed that something was dreadfully wrong.

"I needed to reach him so desperately," she said.

"Why didn't you call him?"

"I did, but I kept getting a recording."

"A recording?" Race looked puzzled. Then she was aware of a profound sympathy in his eyes. "Did it ever occur to you to wonder why it was so difficult for you to reach him?"

"Yes . . ."

His long fingers lifted her chin, and she felt vaguely comforted by his touch. He had shifted his body, and she was aware of his hard thigh pressing against hers. "You don't know, do you?" Race's voice had roughened savagely. "The bastard hasn't had the guts to tell you."

"What?"

"That he's . . ."

The door banged open, and Don, with a young woman as beautifully golden as he, stepped inside the room.

The single word, "married" hung in the hushed

silence, the two syllables burning through Andrea with the stinging fire she'd once felt as a child of three when she'd thrust a bobby pin into an electric socket.

"Married," she finished in a low, dead tone that sounded like a death knell, as she sagged wearily against the hard strength of the man at her side and accepted the comfort of his strong arms.

Chapter 4

"MARRIED." THE WORD THUNDERED IN THE SILENT room, pounded with every painful beat of Andrea's heart, pounded in the faint chiming of the gold and crystal clock on the bureau, pounded in the wind that blew violently up from the sea and rattled the sliding glass door behind the fluttering white curtains.

For one long moment the four people in the suite stared at one another in amazement. The golden woman seemed on the verge of tears.

Andrea wanted to run across the room and throw herself into Don's arms, and scream that it couldn't be true. But some instinct stopped her. Race's arm had wound gently around her slim shoulder, the touch of his warm fingers rigid: Andrea was grateful for his silent strength. The queer expression on the blonde woman's face as she glanced nervously at Don suddenly made it difficult for Andrea to breathe.

"Andy," Race began, in a quiet voice she'd never

heard before, "I want you to meet my brother Don Johnson and his wife, Linda."

"Wife." This horrible truth screamed through her mind and tore at her heart like a ravaging vulture's beak. Then a hideous guilt swamped her as she realized she was in love with another woman's husband.

Andrea grew aware of an awkward silence. The others were waiting for her to speak, and she didn't think she could.

"Hello," she managed at last, very weakly, not lifting her eyes to see the bleak anguish in Don's eyes or the sudden paleness of his wife.

She knew. Andrea, who had the softest of hearts and had never wanted to deliberately inflict pain on any innocent party, realized she had to protect this woman, Don's wife, from any further suffering.

Andrea could scarcely speak, her throat felt so dry and parched, but she forced herself to make the effort. Very slowly, she nuzzled her cheek against Race's shoulder, needing to touch him, hoping his strength would somehow flow into her. Strangely, touching him came so naturally, and she was instantly aware of the quickening of his pulse.

"Race, darling," she murmured as sexily as she could, placing her arms about his neck in a gesture of elaborate intimacy. She trailed a shaking finger down his nape, realizing miserably that she'd never been any good at pretending. "You promised to show me the garden hours ago. Do you mind terribly showing it to me now?" She had to stop; she was too close to tears to go on.

Puzzled, Race gazed down at her, his dark brow lifting, and then he saw the frantic pleading in her sea-green eyes. "Of course, darling," he murmured, regretting it was only a game they were playing. He took one of her hands lightly in his and pressed it gently with a warm, intense kiss.

Andrea felt she was suddenly suffocating with the pressing agony of being inside. Race got up, still holding her hand in his, and helped her to her feet.

She stared wildly toward Don and . . . his wife. "It was so nice to meet you," she rasped, and then she could say no more.

She had to get away from this house, from Don, from the knowledge of his lies both to herself and to his wife. She loved him still . . . she couldn't stop loving him on cue. There were so many questions she wanted the answers for. But she couldn't ask them in front of the one who so rightfully claimed him as her own.

Blindly she stumbled toward the glass doors that led out onto the second tier of terraces. She fumbled with the lock, and then a sure, bronzed hand drew back the curtain and opened the door for her.

Mutely she looked at Race, gratitude and sorrow scrawled on her lovely face. His gaze held hers for a long moment, and it was suddenly very difficult for him to tear himself away from her.

"I'll be out in a minute, little one," he said gently. *Little one.* Odd that he should call *her* that when she was so majestically tall; but in that moment she seemed so tiny and fragile to him, so utterly vulnerable.

For the briefest instant she reached up and brushed his roughened cheek with her lips. Her trembling hands went around his waist and she clung to him, drinking in the comfort of his strong embrace. Just why it seemed so right to kiss him, just why she was so physically drawn to him, she still didn't know.

"Thank you, Race," she murmured sadly, "for being so kind." Then she stumbled outside and collapsed, shaking, against the low wall. Race stared after her, the sight of her pain stabbing his own heart with surprising force.

Below, the Caribbean curled and crashed against a silvery strand of beach and jagged dark fingers of coral.

She stared unseeingly at the beauty of the water, the moonlight shimmering on its surface like liquid white fire. The tears she'd been too proud to shed in front of Don and his wife came then, in great blurring torrents that burned her eyes and scalded her cheeks.

This was the worst mistake she'd ever made—worse even than Enrico; she loved Don in a way she'd never loved Enrico. Even though they'd known each other such a short time, even though they'd never been lovers, she'd given a part of herself to Don she'd never given to any other man. She'd trusted Don as she'd never been able to trust Enrico. And to think that by doing so she'd hurt another woman. She thought of the woman inside, and the terrible pain that she, Andrea, was partially responsible for.

Inside the suite, Race paused beside the open door, the long white curtains swirling around his tall elegantly clad figure. "Linda . . . it's not what you think," Race said gently.

"It's exactly what I think, Race, and you know it. But thank you for trying to spare me. You'll never know how . . ." The brave words began to tremble. "How . . . I . . . I love you for it." She faced her husband. "Don, how could you, again? I thought . . . This time I believed." The agony in her soft voice seared through Race. Then, with a pitifully regal gesture, she squared her shoulders and said proudly, "I'll be downstairs, Don. Waiting. . . ."

Race watched his sister-in-law quietly exit the room; he knew that, though hurt, she was hoping that Don would choose her and join her downstairs.

"Well?" Race's one word was raw with anger. "Which woman is the lucky winner?" he asked sarcastically.

"Linda . . . of course," Don said weakly. "I've really never had any choice, have I?"

"It's a pity you had to drag an innocent party into the

problems of your marriage," Race said. "It was damned cruel of you."

"Go out there, Race," Don begged. "I know I've hurt her. God, I feel like a heel. Take care of her now. . . . Andy's an unbelievably passionate woman, and I don't want to have to answer for what she might do."

A fierce, possessive feeling surged in Race's veins when his brother mentioned Andrea's passionate nature. He remembered the way she'd clung to him so breathlessly at the ballcourt, and then tonight in his bedroom, all the turbulent fire of her emotions communicating her desire to him. He'd felt dazed himself by his own unexpected, too-violent reaction.

He remembered the delicious taste of her delicate lips, her heated response to him when he'd angrily forced his kisses on her earlier in the evening. His anger had melted away and been replaced by the tenderest and most passionate of feelings toward her. Race shook his head, not understanding. He was not completely ready to admit the strength of his desire for this woman who was so different from the women he'd always liked, but he could not deny the disgust he felt at the thought of his brother knowing Andrea intimately.

"Andy's an unbelievably passionate woman." The words burned Race as painfully as the lashings of a whip.

Race shot his younger brother a parting look of scorn and stepped outside, and the balmy heat of the moonlit night wrapped him with its velvet warmth. For a while he stood there staring silently at the slumped figure with the wind-blown green skirts at the wall without knowing what to do or say.

A mixture of baffling emotions stirred in Race—admiration for Andy's attempt to spare Linda the reality of a lover's love for Don despite her own heartbreak, his sympathy for Andy's pain, and, strangest and most surprising of all, jealousy.

Jealousy. That was a painful adolescent emotion he thought he'd left long behind him. Vaguely he remembered a time when he'd been a teenager and lusted after his best friend's girl.

Uneasily Race realized that it bothered him much more deeply than it should have that she loved Don. How much of his anger toward his brother was because of that he didn't know. This woman was turning out to be very different from the selfish, grasping, vain, fortune hunting model he'd believed her to be, and he was beginning to believe that this life would have been far simpler if she'd obliged him by being that malicious schemer.

Putting aside his feelings, Race moved swiftly to her, and his arm gently circled her waist, savoring the soft, feminine feel of her. He felt her body move against his hand with that instinctual physical affinity that was evident between them.

"Andrea, I thought you knew," he said very softly. "I imagined that you wanted to break up Don's marriage. That's why I behaved like such a bastard at Chichén Itzá, and then again tonight."

"You weren't a . . . bastard, either time. I played a part in what happened."

"I shouldn't have been so damned forceful and bullying."

"It doesn't matter, Race," she said weakly, staring out at the sparkling, wind-tossed sea. "Nothing matters anymore. I have no one. I haven't for a very long time. I just didn't know it. You see I thought I had Don. He was so very important to me."

"No one has ever had Don," Race said with uncharacteristic bitterness. "He belongs to the world at large and has great difficulty with intimate relationships."

"Obviously, so do I," she murmured. "Or I would have seen from the first that he was playing a game."

"Don's not always so easy to see through. He deliberately makes that difficult with that sanctimonious smoke-screen of his."

"Funny. I took off three extra weeks, hoping to spend some of that time with Don. But I don't want to go back to New York." She was thinking of the Buick that had almost run her down and the phone calls, and she knew she couldn't face all that feeling as she did. Yet she didn't know what to do. The weeks without Don stretched emptily before her. "I just feel like I can't go on. I feel so alienated, so alone. There's no one now. You couldn't possibly understand. . . ."

Race didn't like the desperate ring in her voice, and he could identify too easily with her feelings. He'd been like that after he'd lost Carolyn. For two years he'd given up everyone and everything, even his painting. "Everyone feels like that from time to time," he said, very gently. "Why don't we go somewhere . . . together? Into town . . . to a crowded bar . . . or somewhere quiet and dark, where we can talk."

She felt very alone. She didn't want to be with anybody, to inflict herself on anyone else; but somehow she knew that it wasn't going to be easy to make Race understand. Still, she had to try. "You're Don's brother . . . I'd rather not be with you . . . or anyone that reminds me of him."

"Don't hold a mere accident of birth against me," Race said, attempting lightness. "Please, will you go into town with me?" he asked again.

"I wouldn't be good company, and I certainly have no right to cry on your shoulder. Your loyalties belong with Linda."

"No, *Don's* loyalties belong with her," Race said firmly, before he thought. Andrea shivered violently as though in pain, and he realized what he'd said. "Sorry."

"It's all right."

"I want to be with you," he said simply, not understanding why this was true. "Will you come with me?"

She turned, and her desolate eyes, liquid with pain, met his. He was a difficult man to say no to. Though she desperately wanted to be alone, there was no fight left in her. "Yes," she managed.

His gaze noted the anguish in her beautiful face. He wished he could think of something to say to ease her suffering. At last he said very gently, "I'm glad you're coming, Andrea. It'll take just a minute to get the car keys. They're inside." She stared at him in helpless silence, and he continued. "Since I paid for a week's rental I still have that car. You see, you did me a favor, unintentional though it was, after all." He smiled down at her before he turned from her and strode toward the mansion.

She couldn't go with him. She was mixed up about Don, but she was confused about Race as well. She needed to be alone.

The minute Race's broad back was to her, she bolted, running so lightly down the steps that he didn't realize she was gone until he stepped inside and found himself alone.

"Damn!" He muttered an unintelligible string of oaths as he pivoted sharply on his heel and ran after her, leaving the doors open so the curtains billowed in the wind.

When was he going to learn she couldn't be trusted for a second?

His footsteps were a thunderous, hollow, clatter as he descended the steps two at a time, sounding, he thought to himself, like a troop of galloping elephants. She could easily hear him coming and conceal herself.

When he reached the lower terrace he had a choice between two staircases that went in opposite directions. He cursed silently again, and then chose the path that led to the beach; he thought he saw a shadow move against a coral knob jutting from a sand dune. It was too far away for him to be sure. It could have been no more than the sweep of a cloud against the moon. He raced toward it, only to discover the beach desolate of all save the scurrying sea creatures and the curl of the surf splashing white froth damply onto the sand.

He turned, looking back toward the red-roofed house with its brilliant lights and dark gardens. His gaze swept over the beach to the dock and *The Jordana*.

Then he saw *her*. Beyond his yacht, in a boat that was far too small for the enormous swells surging into the lagoon.

Damn the woman. Damn her infernal impetuosity.

Suddenly he was cursing himself. Hell! Why was he so damnably stupid? Why hadn't he thought? He knew she'd come by boat.

Race watched helplessly as her small boat skimmed away from the dock, white spume furling in its wake as it plunged toward the turbulence of the open waters crashing into the lagoon. The boat whirled around the reef. He began to run as fast as he'd ever run, despite the difficulties of running on a beach strewn with driftwood and punctured with sharp coral. His dress shoes sank deeply into the thick wet sand and were irrevocably ruined.

He reached the dock, his footsteps sounding heavily on the uneven planking as he shouted to his nephew, sleeping aboard *The Jordana*. "Jake. Jake. Cast off. Now."

A head with hair as black as his own shoved open a window and peered at him groggily. "Uncle Race?"

"Yeah. . . . We're casting off! On the double, boy. Get Felix on deck!"

The normally indolent Jake sprang instantly to life. His uncle's voice was charged with an element he'd heard only once before but had never forgotten—the time when Jake had been a curious three-year-old and toddled dangerously near a diamond-backed rattler. Race had shouted a single word of warning before he'd blown the snake's head off. Jake was still buttoning his levis as he raced on deck barechested.

"There's a crazy girl out there. We're going after her," Race yelled by way of explanation as he snapped on the engines and revved them.

Jake followed his uncle's gaze. "We can't risk going that near the reef, Uncle Race."

"We're going after her."

"Uncle Race. I think she's going down!" Jake screamed as Felix tossed the last dock line free of *The Jordana*'s starboard side as Race carefully backed her away from the dock.

"Jake, don't take your eyes off her," Race yelled.

When Race had the boat safely away from the dock he looked up and saw that a swell crashing over the reef had broached Andrea's little boat and thrown her into the sea. The boat was drifting downwind from the struggling girl. Race's mouth twisted into a sardonic grimace as he skillfully maneuvered *The Jordana* toward the swimmer.

"Damn fool woman!" he muttered to himself. "I've never seen anyone to equal her foolishness. If I've got a grain of sense I'll stay away from her in the future. She lives too dangerously to suit me." Of one thing he was sure: she'd wrenched an incredible amount of drama out of the last forty-eight hours.

Race's face became grave as *The Jordana* surged closer. Andrea was trying to swim back to her boat, but the swift currents kept dragging her in the opposite direction. Suddenly she saw *The Jordana* and her weak gaze lifted to Race's. She tried to smile bravely, but a wave boiled over her and she disappeared in its savage curl.

Race's heart stopped. He held his breath, searching the waves. Finally he saw her head wearily break the surface again. She gasped for air as he realized anew how exhausted she was. She could never swim back to her boat or to his. He couldn't risk taking *The Jordana* any nearer the reef. He was going to have to dive in after her.

He frowned, not liking the thought. He began rapidly unbuttoning his shirt with one hand while he steered with the other. Unbidden came his old fear of sharks, a fear he rarely admitted, for since childhood he'd been scared of only two things. Snakes and sharks. He had no liking for the cool dark Texas Hill Country caves infested with pockets of rattlers, just as he had no desire to swim at night in cool black waters where he couldn't see what was swimming along beside him. His fear, he chided himself weakly as he swiped at the moisture beading his tanned brow so Jake wouldn't see it, was the result of a too-fertile imagination. But as he stared at the ominous, frothing sea, expecting any minute to see a fin break the surface, he remained unconvinced.

"Uncle Race, we can't get any closer," Jake said anxiously, prodding his uncle to take action.

"You're right. Take the wheel. I'm going in after her." Race stripped down to his black briefs, and in the moonlight his massive body seemed nothing but sleek, hard muscle. He grabbed the life ring and climbed up the side of the boat, hesitating only an instant before he plunged head first into the cool, dark waters and began to swim with long powerful strokes toward the woman who was floundering helplessly in the swirling waters.

Saltwater burned his eyes, blurring his vision. He felt the sucking pull of the undertow, the dragging power of the currents that swept along the beaches. Just for an instant he thought he had brushed against something in the water, and his too-fertile imagination obliged him with the image of a snake-eyed shark swimming companionably alongside him observing the flailings of his future dinner. But as Race swam on, still in possession of life and limb, he knew it was but his fear playing tricks on him. Fervently he vowed that if he lived through this, never again would he seek the cheap thrills of going to a movie like *Jaws*.

Andrea choked on sea water as the liquid blackness eddied around her. She thought of Don and their picnics in Central Park. Strangely, she thought of her parents' funeral and the reading of their will. She had been disinherited in favor of her greedy lawyer brother whom her parents had invested with the power of attorney enabling him to write a will favoring himself. Enrico and their joyous marriage day in the little chapel in Greenwich Village came back to her with shuddering clarity as well as a vision of beloved Enrico wrapped in a willowy model's arms in their very own marriage bed. Most surprisingly, she thought of Race and the blazing touch of his lips that had seemed to burn even her soul.

It was over. . . . All the pain . . . all the joy . . . all those tiny little moments of magic that had been her life. She was drifting in a world that was cold and black, and she was utterly and terribly alone.

Race dived for Andrea just as she sank beneath the waves, and he pulled her back up by the ankle. Very slowly he slid the life ring over her head, pulling her limp arms through it so that he could guide her back to *The Jordana*.

It took him twice as long to swim back as it had taken him to reach her. Water continually swept over them, and the currents tugged with insistent force. It was all Race could do to keep Andrea's face out of the water. It lay in the crook of his arm, her red hair streaming in the waves. Her eyes were closed, and her pale face very still. He hoped that she wasn't . . . that he hadn't been too late. He was suddenly very afraid. "Dear God . . ." he mutely beseeched.

For the first time since Carolyn had died in his arms, he prayed.

At last Race reached *The Jordana*. Jake had taken the engine out of gear and lowered the ladder over the stern. Felix was at the wheel while Jake leaned down to assist his uncle. Very gently, Jake took Andrea in his strong brown arms, lifted her over the side into the cockpit and laid her face down on the deck so he could begin artificial respiration. Race swung himself on board, his muscular chest heaving as he gulped in deep breaths. Then he began to shiver in the wind as water streamed off his gleaming body.

"Go below and get her a blanket," Race ordered. "I'll take over." He knelt beside Jake and took Andrea in his arms, carefully cradling her head. He gazed briefly at her small pale face and the curving lips tinged blue from cold. She felt so cool and limp, so very fragile, that her pallor terrified him. He touched his lips to her open mouth, and very deliberately blew air deeply into her lungs.

On the third breath she sputtered to life, gagging weakly and retching salt water. Her eyes fluttered open and she stared up at him in confusion. "Race?" He seemed but part of a dream.

Her head was nestled against his broad chest, and she thought he resembled a certain ancient Greek statue of Poseidon come to life she'd whimsically admired on one of her trips to Crete.

"Don't try to talk . . ." he muttered huskily, aware of an absurdly wild joy that she recognized him.

"I-I thought . . ." Her teeth were beginning to chatter. The cool breeze whirled around them and she snuggled against his naked male flesh for warmth.

Almost fiercely Race wrapped his arms more tightly around her to shield her from the cold.

Race felt the cold from her wet clothing. He glanced impatiently toward the cabin. Where the hell was Jake with those blankets? To her he said very gently, brushing a damp strand of her hair from her forehead, "You're safe, love."

"Love." Funny how she liked him to call her that, as he touched her ever so gently.

"Where am I?"

"On board *The Jordana*."

Suddenly she remembered. She'd only been trying to take her rented boat back to her hotel. If she hadn't been so upset she would have remembered to turn her bow into that wave instead of letting it roll across the boat.

"You must think me an utter fool," she said weakly.

"You'd better not ask my opinion on that score right now," he chided, the faintest of smiles twitching the corners of his mouth. "You haven't the strength to endure the answer."

She tried to smile back at him, but a terrible weakness engulfed her. She sagged against his shoulder. "Sorry . . . so . . . sorry . . ." she murmured apologetically.

Jake's black head appeared in the companionway and he pitched Race a wadded blanket and a couple of towels before going below to take the wheel.

Carefully Race wrapped the blanket around Andrea. Then he lifted her into his arms and carried her below to his stateroom. He had to get her warm and dry as quickly as possible; she seemed very weak. The twofold trauma had obviously exhausted her.

Andrea was vaguely conscious of the lavish furnishings in his stateroom as he pulled aside a scarlet and navy quilted spread and laid her down on his double bunk. She lay back against the pillows, feeling completely worn out. Dark half-moons tinged the delicate skin beneath her eyes. When he brushed her forehead with his palm she felt terribly cold to his touch.

As Race gazed down at her still figure, her features blurred, and instead of her he saw, for an instant, his beloved Carolyn, his beautiful black-haired Carolyn, her beauty gone, her young face ravaged with pain and the long months of her illness.

With an effort he forced himself to shake off the painful memory that still occasionally haunted his nights. Andrea was not ill. She was in no danger. Still, though he hated to disturb her, he knew better than to leave her in her wet clothes. Very gently he reached down and turned her onto her side. His warm fingers slid against her bare skin as he began easing the zipper of her dress down her slender back.

"What are you doing?" she asked warily.

"Taking off your wet clothes."

Green eyes snapped open, and she raised her hand to weakly push against him. When her worried eyes met his black intense gaze, he dropped his hands to his side. As she stared up into his determined handsome face she was too exhausted to protest. The wet chiffon was oozing cold water onto her skin, soaking the blanket and the bed. She was shivering and her teeth chattered. What did conventional modesty matter when she felt so exhausted and cold . . . ? Her hands fell limply to the bed.

"All right," she murmured weakly.

She closed her eyes as though by doing so she was not so conscious of what he was doing. Yet it made her sensually aware of his hands on her body, of their light warm caresses as he removed her clothes.

Race quickly stripped off her gown and her half-slip beneath. He'd noted earlier in the evening (as well as at

Chichén Itzá) that she wore no bra. He wondered if that were a habit with her. Then he rolled her pantyhose down the length of her slender thighs and over the shapely curves of her long legs and narrow ankles. He could not help himself from observing that despite her extreme slenderness she was beautifully formed. Her pale skin was flawlessly smooth, her gentle curves more rounded than he would have thought, her skin pleasantly soft to his touch. The hunger that she'd roused in him earlier flared to fervent heights, but the only sign of it was a faint film of perspiration beading his brow.

Hastily he bundled her naked body beneath the sheets, and drew the covers to her chin. Gathering the thick red masses of her hair, he spread them on her pillow out of her face and tenderly wound them into the softness of a dry towel. Her eyes remained closed, and she had fallen instantly asleep. He couldn't know how she had reveled in the gentleness of his skillful ministrations.

As soon as he had her settled, he stripped out of his own wet underwear which he tossed on top of her wet gown. He moved about the room hurriedly, for her presence in his bed disturbed him.

Briefly Andrea's eyes drowsily fluttered open. She was startled when her vision was filled with his bronzed male nudity. Even when he turned and caught her looking at him, and she blushed like a modest virgin, she couldn't bring herself to tear her eyes away. Dreamily she wondered if he thought her curiosity about his body as unseemly as he'd thought her desire for him earlier. But in that moment she didn't care. He was perfectly formed, and she liked looking at him. She liked the lazy grace of his great body, the golden-brown hue of his smooth, dark skin, the ripple of his well-toned muscles.

"You're beautiful," she stated quietly, scarcely realizing that she spoke aloud, closing her eyes then in deep contentment, the vision of his bronzed maleness lingering. "So beautiful."

"So are you," he said, pulling on a pair of dry trousers before he moved toward her and smiled gently down at her. There was an intimacy between them, the intimacy that belongs only to lovers.

She scarcely dared open her eyes again, sensing his nearness. There was something so bewilderingly intense about him and her own feelings for him.

She heard the deep melody of his Texas drawl caressing her. "Little one, how would you like to spend those three free weeks of yours in Texas, with me? On my ranch?"

She opened her eyes; she had to read his expression. To her surprise she saw that his dark face was gravely sincere. "Race . . . I couldn't impose on you like that," she replied softly, deeply appreciating his kindness in offering.

"You wouldn't be imposing on me. I have a guest house behind the main house, so you would have complete privacy."

"It's not just a question of that."

"I want you to come to Texas. You see, I feel responsible for you. Because of Don. I'd worry about you if you didn't come. I don't think you should be alone right now. I—I know what that's like."

"I can't let you. . . ."

"Of course you can. Besides, you owe me, for saving your life."

"Owe you?"

"For risking my neck in those shark-infested waters." There was the hint of a smile in his voice.

"There aren't any sharks out there."

"Says who?" She glanced up at him and saw that he was serious.

"You were really afraid?" she ventured hesitantly.

"I don't suppose I should admit it," he said. He knelt beside the bed and arranged the covers beneath her throat, his long fingers lightly caressing her skin. "It doesn't seem very macho."

She smiled weakly. "I'm really sort of glad you did."

"Come to Texas and model for me," he said in a more serious tone.

"I don't understand."

"I want to paint you."

"I still don't understand."

He wasn't sure he wanted her to, but there seemed no way to avoid telling her who he was. "That's because you don't know who I am," he said at last. "I'm *George* Jordan, the painter."

George Jordan. . . . The conversation was too complex for her exhausted mind, but she struggled to concentrate on what he was saying. With an effort she opened her eyes again and stared incredulously up at him. She knew the name, as who did not. He was a vastly successful and prolific artist with varied techniques, a legend in his own time. His paintings hung in museums all over the world, even in the USSR, and were avidly sought by wealthy collectors.

"*The* George Jordan?"

"Yes." There was an amused dryness in his deep tone at the awe he read in her drowsy stare. "I see you're properly impressed."

"But . . . ?" She wrinkled her nose. "I thought he was old."

He smiled that devastatingly white smile of his. "Disappointed?"

"No. But you paint all those nudes, and they have such magnificent figures. Big bosoms and hourglass waists. Have your tastes in models changed suddenly? Do you expect me to model for you . . . with nothing on?"

"That would, of course, be an added pleasure for

me." She felt the searing warmth of his hand brush her
face. His eyes went over her, and she felt that he was
imagining what lay beneath the sheet. "Your body is
very beautiful, but what I had in mind was a portrait."

"Oh."

Why did she feel oddly deflated?

"Surely a portrait couldn't be offensive to you," he
persisted.

"No . . . it's not that."

"Will you come with me then?" She was aware of
him watching her intently as though her answer deeply
mattered to him.

She nodded feebly, the conversation having exhausted her ability to say no to him. The dry sheets tucked
about her nude body felt so comforting. A delicious,
warm lassitude was enveloping her like a bank of soft
clouds shrouding her mind. George Jordan. . . .
Imagine . . . she thought vaguely, since she deeply
admired his work. To be painted by him would be a
great honor, and perhaps she could learn something she
could bring to her own art.

"I think I've known I had to paint you from the
moment I saw you," he whispered. But she didn't hear
him; she was already asleep, smiling as she drifted off.
Nor did she feel the warmth of his lips against her own
when he brushed them tenderly with a kiss, or the heat
of his hands tucking the coverlets around her, hands
that lingered too long and too intimately upon her.

Race's most acute critic, Sam Sanderson, a New
York dealer Race trusted implicitly, had said cryptically not a week ago, "Race, there's a reason for your
huge success, old boy. You never choose to paint a
subject that you aren't deeply involved with. Good
painters don't paint with brushes. They paint with their
hearts."

Race stared down at the sleeping woman in his bed,
more deeply disturbed than he wanted to admit even to

himself. From the moment he'd taken her in his arms at the ballcourt there had been a strange bond of intimacy between them.

Until he'd met Andrea two days ago, his life had been on the same placid keel it had been on for the past five years. He had his work, his ranch, and time off on *The Jordana*. And then, of course, there was his very comfortable relationship with Rebecca. All in all he'd been pleased with his well-ordered life.

Suddenly he had the oddest feeling that if he took Andrea to Texas, nothing would ever be quite the same again.

Sam's words came back to haunt him. "Good painters paint with their hearts."

Race hadn't wanted to paint a woman since his Carolyn, and he couldn't stop himself from wondering why it suddenly seemed so important to him that he paint Andrea.

Chapter 5

RACE LEFT ANDREA SLEEPING IN HIS BUNK AND CLIMBED up to the deck. Jake and Felix were in the process of docking *The Jordana,* so Race grabbed the boat hook and began moving swiftly to retrieve the dock lines. He saw that Jake had managed to secure the bow line of Andrea's rented boat to a stern cleat, and had towed it back to shore.

When the men had the yacht tied up, Ross said, "We're leaving for Texas in, say, an hour, Jake. Tell Felix." ·

"In one hour?" Jake stared at him, gaping at this unexpected news. "What . . . what are we going to do with *her?*" He nodded toward the cabin below, meaning Andrea.

"Miss Ford's going with us."

"Why?"

Race glared at his thunderstruck nephew in sudden

impatience. "Since when do I have to explain everything I do?"

Jake could be as stubborn as his uncle. He crisscrossed his arms against his muscular chest in a defiant stance.

"Since you came up with this damn-fool peculiar notion of taking that half-drowned girl clear to Galveston in the middle of the night—with me on board! I don't want any part of it."

"Look, she's got nowhere else to go," Race explained more reasonably. "That's all. She's agreed to go. She wants to. It's a long story, and it involves your Uncle Don."

"Oh."

"I need to get her out of Mexico and away from Don before he decides to do something rash. Get the picture?"

Jake knew all about his Uncle Don and his women; the odd thing about this episode was that usually his Uncle Race disliked Don's women.

Jake nodded. "Yeah. I get the picture, in living color. So what do you want me to do?"

"Make sure we've got enough fuel, and take care of her boat while I go ashore and set things straight with Don. Call the people she rented it from, make the necessary financial arrangements, and have them pick it up over here."

"Aye, aye." Jake touched two fingers to his forehead in a mock salute.

Race's black eyes twinkled. "And cut the sarcasm."

"Aye. . . ."

"I said . . ."

"Okay. So a chick's finally gotten into you again. Funny, 'cause she sure isn't half the looker Rebecca is."

Race whirled to face the impertinent twenty-year-old youth. "What the hell did you say?"

Jake stifled his smile. "I said that I'll be ready in an hour, Captain Blye."

"Good." Race, too, worked to suppress his smile.

The Jordana rolled with the deep swells as she headed due east into the open Caribbean to avoid the reefs that edged the coast. When they were far enough from shore, they would turn north and head for the Yucatan Strait before plotting a northwesterly course across the Gulf of Mexico.

Navigational charts were spread open beside Race where he had been studying them. Jake watched his uncle anxiously as Race refolded the charts and began studying the radar screen before he deftly switched on the loran and set the way point for the entrance to the Galveston ship channel.

The small island *Isla Mujeras* to port was clearly visible on radar. They were at least four days and four nights from Galveston.

Race had thoughtfully equipped *The Jordana* with such sophisticated electronics that the autopilot could be turned on and connected with the loran, and the boat could steer itself to its destination without ever veering off course. Of course, it was still up to the captain to follow his charts and thereby avoid running aground on shoals or reefs, note the numbers on Long Range markers, avoid collisions with other vessels, and monitor the electronic equipment in case it failed. Both Jake and Race were experienced seamen, and frequently crewed together in the summers when they went shrimping or fishing in the Gulf.

"Why don't you go below," Jake suggested, "and let me take the wheel, since I've already gotten four or five hours' sleep."

"Okay." Race was anxious to check on Andrea, who'd been asleep for more than two hours.

Race was instantly alarmed when he let himself into

his darkened stateroom and heard Andrea's laborious, snuffling breaths filling the silence. It sounded as if she might be taking cold from her chilly swim. He quickly strode to the bed and placed his palm on her forehead. Her skin was faintly warm to his touch.

"Please," she murmured, only half-opening her eyes, "I'm so v-very c-cold." Her teeth chattered, and she was shivering. He noted that her slender body was coiled in a tight ball beneath the covers in a vain attempt to warm herself.

He stared down at her, trying to think what to do.

Her hand reached up and closed gently around his wrist. "Please . . ." she begged, shuddering.

He hesitated no longer. Quickly undressing, he slid into bed beside her. He gathered her into his broad arms and lay back with her upon the pillows. Beneath the musty covers he immediately felt uncomfortably warm, but despite his own discomfort, he bundled Andrea's shivering body tightly against his body. Lord. It felt like a furnace.

Weakly, she buried her face against the heated hollow of his throat in gratitude, her every breath rasped painfully against his skin. Her flaming hair spilled over his shoulders, a few wispy strands tickling his nose and causing him to sneeze. She groaned in pain at his abrupt movement, and he patted her bright head, whispering soothing words.

His soft, comforting tone seemed to ease her; he felt her slender hands clutch him as she adjusted her body to fit his so that her bare breasts fused with the hardness of his sun-bronzed chest. Her dainty slender body fitted his as though they had been made for each other. He liked the lightness of her, the delicacy of her, the exciting strangeness of her.

Rosy nipples tautened against the matted hairs of his chest, or did he only imagine their pressure? He groaned aloud, as he felt sudden, acute desire for her, quickly followed by intense self-disgust. He was not used to nobly sharing a bed with a woman who was not his lover. He must force his mind to some safe topic.

The woman was weak and ill, in need of his protective care. Still he could not stop his growing awareness of her as a woman, the sweet-smelling womanly scent of her, the way she gently clutched him, seeking the delicious warmth of his body. He liked holding her in his arms much more than he should have.

Despite the wretched heat of the bed, the rocking motion of the boat lulled Race's senses. A dreamy languor stole over him. He fell asleep, wrapped in Andrea's feverish arms.

The rosy streamers of dawn's first light sifted through the curtained portholes. Andrea grew slowly aware of unfamiliar sounds and sensations, the incredible warmth of the comforting cocoon in which she slept, the continual roar of *The Jordana's* engine, the faint roll of the sea, the perpetual creakings of the yacht.

Andrea shifted lazily, feeling stiff and hot. She threw aside the sheet and then snuggled more deeply into the hard warmth of her pillow. Something felt vaguely wrong . . . but so deliciously right. Slowly her eyelids fluttered drowsily open, and she realized that the pillow wasn't a pillow, but the broad expanse of a man's chest.

Beneath her ear pounded the steady drumbeat of Race's heart. She caught the scent of him. Black curling hairs scratchily brushed her cheek. Her fingers were wound around his neck while his strong arms were draped intimately over her body, one of his hands cupping her breast in a familiar caress. Masculine tanned thighs were intertwined with her own pale legs. Every part of him seemed to be touching her. And a faint film of mingled perspiration coated their skin.

She blushed as a hot raw flame burned through her, aware of the quickening of her pulse. What was he doing in bed with her? Holding her as though she belonged to him? Had he? Had they? Or had he slept with her simply because there was no other bed, letting sleep erase the normal boundaries of propriety they would have otherwise observed. Her blush deepened as she searched her hazy memory for the answer to her questions. It was difficult to think clearly, but she couldn't remember anything out of the ordinary. Still, to wake up naked in the arms of a stranger. . . .

She reached for the sheet she had cast aside so she could cover the positively indecent exposure of her flesh. And his. But when she tried to extricate herself from his embrace, she found that she was pinned so thoroughly beneath him and that her legs were so completely mingled with his that she could not wiggle free without touching him even more intimately.

She would have to wake him. "Race?" She stroked her fingers through the springy thickness of his hair, liking the softness of its texture and the way it curled around her fingers like strands of black silk. There were shadows beneath his eyes. He looked tired, and a faint sympathy for all that she'd put him through stirred in her. Very gently she traced her finger down his grizzled unshaven cheek, exploring the masculine planes of his rugged face. Her soft fingertip moved delicately around the edges of his mouth, outlining its shape.

"Mmmmm." He was trying to ignore her efforts to waken him; she felt his hand close possessively over her breast, rubbing the soft, velvety tip as though even in his sleep he liked the feel of caressing its pliant softness.

Every nerve in her body tingled when he touched her thus, and she didn't try to squirm free or brush his hand away nearly so quickly as she should have.

"Race?" She tried to slip away from him, but his arm around her tightened to press her even more closely against his body. She felt every burning inch of his warmly moistened skin where it touched hers. She was

disturbingly aware of the hardness of him, the maleness
of him, the beginning of his growing arousal.

"Where are you going?" he inquired sleepily, holding her still.

"I . . . we shouldn't be like this," she said huskily.

"Why?" he murmured drowsily. "When it's so enjoyable?"

"We shouldn't be here in bed, together," she insisted.

"You should have thought of that last night, before
you invited me to join you," he teased, awakening.

"I did?" To her dismay he nodded, grinning broadly,
his expression so alert she suspected him of playing
opossum. "Well, I didn't know what I was doing," she
snapped, growing irritable at the way he so obviously
relished this situation which she was finding increasingly embarrassing.

"Hmmmm. For one who didn't know what she was
doing, you've proven yourself quite a talented little
bedwarmer." He opened his eyes and let them drift
lazily downward over the rumpled white sheet that
concealed the intimate tangle of their bodies. She felt
his hand caress the smooth curve of her hips in a
familiar fashion.

She gasped in horror. "Don't do that. Take your
hands off me!"

He reached a palm up to brush her cool forehead.
"You must be feeling better," he said, his concern for
her so evident in his deep voice that some of her anger
abated.

"I feel fine. A little tired."

"I think I like you best when you're asleep," he
mused. "You were very affectionate, clinging to me,
pleading with me to take you in my arms." His mocking
eyes pierced her defenses.

"I was!"

She stared at him, open-mouthed, thoroughly

shocked. He had the advantage over her, of course, and it amused him to play it to the hilt. He knew what had happened between them, while she did not.

She lurched bolt upright into a rigid sitting position, trying not to notice the way her lower body erotically slid across his. But deep in the corner of her female mind, a charged awareness of his masculinity registered strongly. The sheet fell to her waist, exposing her small breasts to his appreciative view. Her cheeks were aflame with ire and embarrassment. Then his warm chuckle vibrated through her, and she felt the heat of his devouring gaze as it traveled in lazy male admiration over her female form, from the round softness of her breasts to the gentle curving of her narrow waist and rounded belly. A wave as hot as fire swept through her. In fury she yanked the sheet primly back over her.

In her profession she'd thought she'd long ago lost all her modesty, since she appeared frequently in a state of semi-undress in front of men. But those men never looked at her as Race did. Nor had she ever had the misfortune to awaken and find herself in bed with one of them, to find her body warmed so thoroughly by the heat of his. None of them had ever made her feel so . . . hot and quivery . . . and so thoroughly confused.

"Don't you even feel a qualm of embarrassment to be like this with me?" she asked in a fractured voice.

"Not a qualm," he replied easily.

"Not even when we scarcely know each other."

"Oh, that's not true, any longer."

"What do you mean?" Green eyes widened.

"What?" He was grinning, and that infuriating eyebrow of his was arched; he was devilishly handsome.

"That we made love?" The very words trembled.

Still smiling, he studied her distraught face. "Would that be so awful, making love to me?"

In a frozen moment of suspended time she sensed the

depth to his question, the importance of her answer to him. And to her.

Beneath his intent gaze she went scarlet. "Of course, I'd think it awful," she stammered, feeling self-conscious suddenly for fear he would see too clearly she was not being honest with him. "We have no feelings for one another."

"None at all?" he mocked, bringing a callused finger up to circle the gentle swell of her pink-tipped breast beneath the sheet, before she jumped breathlessly away, a wave of unadulterated sensual pleasure shuddering through her. "None, you say?" Knowing amusement laced his deep tone.

"None other than . . ."

She couldn't deny that in some primitive man-woman way she was attracted to him. Nor could she admit, even to herself, how special he could so effortlessly make her feel, how his smile could light up her whole being.

"Than . . . lust?" he finished amicably, his black eyes twinkling.

"Dàmn it!" She choked on the words, angry because of her vulnerability. "Are you going to tell me what happened last night or not?"

"Suppose I told you that no Moslem sultan ever found the seduction of his most prized houri more delightful than I found you last night."

She gasped at this horrifying statement.

He began to laugh then as she purpled in embarrassment, and only when she glared at him did he force himself to stop. "Your lack of enthusiasm is hardly flattering," he said ruefully. She merely scowled more deeply at him. "No, little one. Alas, tempting as you are, you were ill and cold, and I'm afraid my behavior was disappointingly chivalrous. It is not my habit to bed unconscious women."

She was sighing in deep relief when he reached for

her, and pulled her face back down to his level. "I'm glad you're no longer unconscious or feverish, and there's no longer any need for my . . . er . . . chivalrous abstinence in that department. Because I'm in acute need of you." He laughed softly. "Perhaps it's time we did . . . get to know each other better. Since that seems to be bothering you so much."

Andrea opened her mouth to protest, but warm, gentle lips closed over hers and the words rumbled backwards, dying in her throat. Bedsheets rustled as he rolled her underneath him, his skilled hands adjusting her delicate body intimately beneath his own that was rock hard and powerful. He was an utterly aroused male. A palpable tremor of sensual pleasure rocked her body. She was all too wantonly aware of his violent masculine need of her, and her own body achingly betrayed her with long-suppressed needs of its own. He lay sprawled on top of her and the gentle, rhythmical motion of the boat rocked their bodies up and down.

He forced her mouth open, and his tongue probed the delectable honeyed sweetness of her mouth. Arms that came up to push him away trembled and then slid around his powerful neck and clung to the hard male contours with hedonistic abandon.

He kissed her deeply, savoring the taste of her while his hands stroked the fragrant flesh of her throat and her creamy shoulders. He bent low and softly kissed one rose petal-pink nipple. She shivered beneath the skill of his tantalizingly delicate touch.

Race accepted his desire as the natural consequence of having slept with her on such intimate terms the evening before. He'd awakened time and again throughout the long night to find her feminine body pressing tightly against his, her legs and arms laced intimately with his, her small breasts pushing warmly against his furred chest, her hands touching him in places that would have made her blush had she been conscious of their familiar roamings. It had taken all his willpower to stay his desire when her breathing had regulated and her shivering had ceased. But he'd known she was exhausted.

He'd wanted her in a basic masculine way, and at the moment he no longer saw any reason to deny his feelings. His lips wandered over her flesh as he practiced the gentle method of arousal at which he was so skilled. Despite the urgency of his own need he viewed sex with her as a pleasure he intended to enjoy to its limits, rather than as a conquest to be hastily made. She was a rare delicacy to be nibbled slowly to fully experience every nuance of her sensual flavor. Lightly his lips caressed each rosy peak until it stood temptingly erect. Then his mouth moved up to cover the pulsebeat pounding in the warm hollow of her throat. She drove him wild: beneath the fire of her he sensed her vulnerability and the softness of her gentle heart.

How soft his touch was, Andrea thought, how pleasingly hard and warm his body. Race's lean, brown fingers skimmed lightly over her breasts and hips, fondling her, his hand sliding between the creaminess of her white thighs. His lips plundered her mouth, his tongue savagely searching its warm moist interior. Andrea was sinking into a blissful haze of sensation. Her sense of reality dissolved, and she was only aware of the strong man whose kisses branded her with the fire of his passionate possession, whose muscular body was molded to hers.

Above, at the wheel, Jake leaned away from the breeze gusting through the window to light his cigarette. A wave slapped the side of the yacht with a fierce crack, and the boat rolled more precariously than usual. Then the vessel righted itself immediately and plowed more smoothly through the water.

Still, the wave had jolted Andrea's languid world just

enough to awaken a tiny logical voice that had been slumbering.

"What am I doing?"

Andrea forced her eyelids open. She forced herself to think, to concentrate. It was very difficult since she felt drugged, her passion a powerful narcotic, each quivering sensation when male lips brushed her love-sensitized flesh a stronger dose of the same addicting drug. Involuntarily she arched her body to meet his questing lips even as her mind began its battle.

"I can't, I mustn't let this happen." Hot lips slid over the warmth of her pliant flesh, and she shuddered with the exquisite rapture they evoked. The tiny voice in the depths of her mind persisted. "Even if it seems like Heaven on earth."

Determinedly she tried to struggle free of the sensual stimuli that wracked her body with such delightfully pulsing sensations.

"Race . . ." she murmured very weakly against his mouth. "Please stop."

Race lifted his head in mild astonishment, his black eyes intent as they studied her yielding expression. Her response to him was so complete he scarcely believed his ears. Her mouth was half-opened, her head back against the pillow, her tortured breaths unevenly spaced, her slender body trembling beneath his. Yet she said stop. He exhaled a ragged breath in impatience. "It's too late to stop," he responded at last, before he lowered his mouth once more to the trembling lips that parted invitingly to accept his tongue.

Her entire body shuddered; she forced herself to freeze in his arms, drawing her mouth from the seductive pleasures of his.

"I want you, too," she admitted hesitantly. "I don't know why. I don't understand how it's possible. How this is possible."

"Remind me to loan you a book on biology."

"I'm serious, Race."

"So am I." He smiled. "Why do we have to understand it?" he queried, as his tongue toyed with the velvet edge of her earlobe in sensual persuasion.

"But I don't want this to happen between us," she replied softly. "In the first place it isn't fair to you. I think I'd just be using you."

He shrugged good humoredly. "Go ahead and use me, lady. I'm all yours." His lips swooped down and covered her warm mouth agreeably again, hoping to silence her.

Gently she pushed him away, and he reluctantly let her. Her fingers came up to lovingly trace the line of his jaw while she spoke, his unshaven skin coarse beneath her fingertips. Oddly, his face was very dear to her. She loved touching him, looking at him, being near him. She didn't want to hurt him.

"Race, I'm still in love with Don," she said very quietly, not liking his instant stillness, the queer intensity of his gaze. Funny, she hadn't once thought of Don and their painful encounter yesterday, until this moment. It was so difficult to think of any other man when Race was near. But that was only because subconsciously she must be using him deliberately to forget Don. She forced herself to go on. "I can't just stop loving him, no matter how much I want to."

Race's dark expression hardened before he turned his head away. For a moment she wondered if she'd hurt him. She felt the sudden tension in his body, his deliberate mental withdrawal.

Race didn't like being reminded she'd been his brother's woman; the mere thought of it galled him. He laughed suddenly, thinking himself a fool for his misplaced desire, for the tenderness he felt toward her. Hell, he had better reasons than she to avoid getting involved with her. It was not a pleasant laugh. "If this isn't the damnedest—" He broke off, his black eyes hard when they met hers.

She looked very small and young in his arms, her hair spilling like flames over his bronzed skin. Two days ago he'd set a trap for her, and he was beginning to wonder if he'd caught himself in it. "Whatever you want, my dear," he said, forcing a negligence he was far from feeling into his voice. "If you wish to cherish memories of my brother, I'll be the first to leave you to them."

Her expression flickered. His words brought pain, but she tried to mask it.

Race felt an unbearable need to get away from her, and he would have swung himself free of her and the bed except her fingers gently closed over his hand. For some unfathomable reason he let her restrain him.

"Race, please try to understand." There was something so tender in her voice it touched his heart.

"It isn't just Don. If there were no Don, you and I wouldn't even be here in the first place! If I hadn't run from you last night and nearly drowned, you would never have thought it necessary to bring me on board your yacht, and into your bed. I'm not blaming you. This is as much my fault as yours. I've never gotten so quickly involved with any man as I have you—not even the man I married. My divorce taught me how disastrous it can be getting involved with a man only because of a sexual attraction."

Logically, he knew she was right, but Race wasn't feeling particularly logical at the moment.

"That's why I fell for Don in the first place," she continued. "He was so different from Enrico. He seemed so special."

"If you think I want you to recount all the details of your past love life, you're dead wrong," Race said angrily, not wanting to hear about Don and how special he had been.

Instantly she realized that no man wanted to hear

about the other men a woman had known. But how could she begin to explain?

"What I'm trying to say, Race, is that I've never hopped into bed with any man on the third day that I've known him—just on animal impulse. I think things have gotten way out of hand between us. But I do have feelings for you that I don't understand. I . . ."

"Animal impulse." He didn't like the term when she applied it to her feelings about him. Race's black eyes raked over her insolently; he saw her obvious distress. Suddenly he smiled faintly, forcing reason to prevail over his anger, and his arm slid beneath her thick hair and encircled her slim shoulder.

"You know what," he began. "I don't understand my feelings for you any more than you do." He bent his head so their foreheads touched. She felt his fingers in her hair.

"Why don't we leave it at that? We can take things more slowly from here on." He pulled away. Lightly, he brushed her forehead with his lips in a gesture that was infinitely tender, and then got out of bed.

She felt a vague sense of disappointment to be left alone in his bed, a strange enveloping sense of forlornness that she didn't understand.

He dressed quickly, not speaking as though he were in a hurry to get away from her. Despite the knowledge that she shouldn't, she watched him; she liked watching him.

Once when he looked toward her. She made no chaste effort to avert her gaze from his bronzed virility.

"For a girl who distrusts sexual attraction, you certainly aren't trying very hard to curb your own prurient interest."

She flushed as bright as the red roots of her hair. Recovering herself, she forced a pert smile and then mocked him with his own turn of phrase. "You're not

the only one with an . . . a rather flawed, shall I say,
character. We just have different weaknesses."

He laughed then. "My dear, I'm not so sure we do,"
he drawled in amused rejoinder, his black eyes drinking
in the sight of her female body so wantonly displayed,
her long silken form she had not bothered to cover.

She felt relieved and happy his good humor was
apparently restored, and she smiled at him as she
pulled the sheet over herself.

He grinned down at her. "I'll have to find you
something to wear, my dear, so that I won't be so sorely
tempted to give into that latest weakness of mine."

Then he was gone, and she was left blushing, her
heart pounding with that unnerving excitement he
could so easily arouse. She remembered Enrico and
their initial fiery attraction. Feelings like these hot
treacherous tides were not to be trusted. She knew
that, of course. Race was a man of sensual appetites,
and she was but a convenient means of satisfying one of
them.

If she were smart she would pack her bags the minute
they docked in Galveston. What bags? she thought
rebelliously, finding this logical plan strangely abhor-
rent. Discounting his overpowering sexual charisma,
Race was George Jordan, and he wanted to paint her.
She could learn a lot from such an experience.

"He's a lot more than you bargained for," that tiny
voice at the back of her mind warned.

It had long been a habit of hers to ignore that voice
when it ran counter to what she really wanted to do.

She might never have the chance again to come so
close to artistic genius. Never before had she been to a
ranch in Texas, and surely the opportunity to model for
a world-famous artist on a secluded Texas ranch was as
exotic a way to spend one's time as trekking about the
world alone to view famed architectural wonders.

She was rationalizing, of course; she wanted to go with him. Why shouldn't she? Besides, when had she ever said no when an exotic adventure beckoned?

As she waited for Race to return with something for her to wear, she knew that despite her misgivings she rather liked feeling as she did when Race was near, more wildly alive than she'd ever felt before. It was like that breathless feeling one has when one steps too near the edge of a cliff and the bottom drops out of one's stomach. Once as a child, when she'd visited a zoo, she'd wandered too dangerously near a tiger's cage and experienced that same thrilling sensation.

Andrea didn't dwell on the fact she was growing involved with a man who might have no place for her in his life.

Three weeks in Texas at a remote ranch.

That tiny logical voice in the back of her mind refused to shut up.

She was insane to go with Race, no matter how badly she felt because of Don. Now that she was aware of her intense and volatile feelings for Race. At any moment they might erupt out of control.

But when she considered her alternative, it seemed scarcely less dangerous. Too vividly she recalled that hoarse, midnight voice that had sadistically threatened her as well as that great Buick careening toward her like a black devil on wheels. Just the thought of those terrors, and she shivered. Of the two dangers, Race was definitely the more attractive.

She couldn't go back to New York. Not yet. She wasn't ready to cope with whatever awaited her there, and she didn't want to travel alone. She'd thought she would be with Don, not by herself.

Don. Strange how he now seemed like a shadowy figure from the past. And it had been only yesterday that she'd been so sure of her love for him.

It was so difficult to concentrate on Don that she

gave up the attempt. Suddenly, she was thinking instead of the virile man she'd slept with. A rush of warm color stained her cheeks as she thought of Texas and going there with Race.

She had to go with him. It was that simple. She didn't understand why, she just had to. Andrea lay back, and a dreamy smile tilted her lips provocatively as she tried to suppress the ripe imagination that kept trying to contemplate what might happen between them if she were not very very careful.

With superhuman effort, she pushed the disturbing visions of herself wrapped against the hard warmth of Race's masculine body out of her mind. That wouldn't happen again. She would be cautious; she would not give in to an attraction that for her could only have devastating consequences.

Never once did it occur to her that hers was the last personality to be cautious.

Chapter 6

RACE PLAYED THE ROLE OF GALLANT GENTLEMAN DISAP-
pointingly well, Andrea discovered during the next two
days and nights, as they sped across the Gulf of Mexico.
Not once did he even come close to making a pass at
her. It was almost as if the sensual night they had
passed together had never occurred. She watched un-
happily as he'd removed his clothes from his stateroom,
gallantly telling her he would sleep in another one
down the hall near Jake's.

Because Jake was tall and slim, like Andrea, he'd
loaned her several pairs of his jeans, which she'd had to
gather with a belt around her much narrower waist.
When she wore the faded cotton shirts she'd borrowed,
she bound them tightly around her midriff, tying the
corners of the shirt tightly together beneath her
breasts. Jake's arms and legs were longer than hers, and
she had to roll deep cuffs in the pants legs to expose
slim ankles and push her billowy shirt sleeves up to her

elbows. In the course of her profession she'd acquired that rare ability of knowing how to wear clothes so that any garment she put on, no matter how unappealing in itself, acquired instant panache.

"I must look like Robinson Crusoe," she'd said playfully to Race that first day she wore the apparel and altered the masculine clothes to her feminine shape.

Race's black gaze had flitted over her lithe body reflectively, liking what he saw far too much. Instantly he curbed the hot emotion that coursed in his veins. "Not exactly," he replied hoarsely before he turned quickly away and attempted to study a chart and plot their exact position, his manner that of a man in the presence of a woman whose appearance did not interest him in the least.

She'd felt hurt by his obvious rejection, but this action proved typical of the offhand way he was determined to treat her. While he was friendly and helpful, he deliberately kept his distance, spending most of his time with Jake and Felix. She felt frustrated and out of sorts, yet didn't understand why she should feel that way. Hadn't she told him she was still in love with his brother, that she wasn't ready for any deep involvement with him? What did she expect, that he fall at her feet like a lovesick teenager so she could brush him off again?

Race was a man of immense energy, and the running of *The Jordana* was a task he thoroughly enjoyed. "It's one of the ways I sweep the cobwebs out of my mind," he'd laughingly confided to her in one of those rare moments when he'd dropped his guard with her. He'd helped her up beside him then, his brown arm carelessly draped around her bare waist, his thigh fitted snugly against hers. She'd revelled in that stolen moment of togetherness when all the barriers between them had slipped away. That brilliant afternoon on the glistening gulf waters, he taught her to steer the boat, regaling her with stories of his adventures on the Gulf. He'd laughed down at her, and she'd basked in his masculine attention.

When he wasn't involved with the boat, he kept busy sketching. She learned not to bother him when he was thus occupied, for the work necessitated his absolute concentration.

Andrea pitched in and turned herself into a first-rate galley slave. Race had taught her to use the gimboled alcohol stove as well as the oven. The first afternoon, when the men were busy topside, she even baked an angel food cake; since all the cake mixes on board were of that variety, there had been no choice. Race, Jake, and Felix had devoured it with gusto that night, and when questioned as to why there had been three boxes of that same flavor, Race wryly admitted that angel food cake was his favorite dessert.

She immediately baked the other two cakes. It pleased her in some curiously womanly way to cook for him and bring him such pleasure by doing so. In the past she'd shunned domestic pursuits, and she found this change in herself perplexing.

The perpetual roll of the boat was something that Andrea found very difficult to get used to. It made her feel weak and queasy, and all too often she had to clamber up to the side of the boat and lean over, waiting for her nausea to pass. Whenever possible she kept her eyes glued to the horizon, because that alone seemed to help the rumbling uneasiness of her stomach.

She'd tried valiantly to keep her discomfort a secret, for the last thing she wanted to do was to burden Race with her illness. But the first afternoon he found her looking pale and greenish as she collapsed against the side of the boat after a particularly violent bout of her sickness.

"Why didn't you tell me," he'd asked gently.

She reddened with humiliation. "I didn't want you to think . . ."

"You little fool," he'd chided tenderly, drawing her damp head against his chest when the queasiness had subsided. "Did you really think I'd think less of you for that? Some of the best sailors I've ever known get seasick with the greatest regularity."

"They do?" His hands in her hair felt very soothing, and she wanted to prolong this time of comforting nearness.

Unfortunately he did not; he drew away from her as soon as some color returned to her cheeks.

"I've got Dramamine down below in the medicine chest."

She hadn't realized he could so easily solve her problem. He gave her all the tablets in the box, and she gobbled one every time she had a new attack. The pills left her drowsy; she lazed through the days, taking frequent naps, falling asleep in odd positions on the shaded deck, only to awaken an hour later and discover that someone had tucked a blanket about her and a pillow beneath her head, or moved her chair into the shade when the angle of the sun had changed because she burned so easily. As the days passed she didn't tell Race how rapidly the supply of pills he'd given her was diminishing. Perhaps by the time she ran out of them, she would have grown accustomed to the motion.

It was the evening of the third night. Andrea was drying dishes, and the men were all on deck. The moon hadn't come up, and only a single fluorescent light shone in the galley. Outside, except for the faint green and red running lights, all was soft blackness.

If it weren't for her seasickness and her knowledge that she had only three little white pills left, and Race's disturbing presence, the cruise would have been idyllic. Andrea understood what Race had meant when he'd said that the sea was a method of sweeping away mental cobwebs. She'd scarcely thought of the unresolved terror that awaited her in New York. Nor had she thought of Don. These three days had been like an island of time separating her from the realities of life.

Of course, when she chanced to catch sight of Race, she was never able to wholly suppress the disturbing memory of that sultry morning when she'd awakened in bed with him, their naked bodies entwined as intimately as though they were lovers. She had to steel herself to remain calm in his presence. Always she had to fight that quicksilver feeling his roguish virility so easily aroused, to fight that strange dangerous desire to touch him.

A noise from the companionway startled her, and she whirled, her face aglow in the soft light, her eyes brilliant and expectant as they met Race's.

"I didn't know you were there," she managed in a breathless voice.

As always, her determination to remain immune to his dark good looks was dissolving, just as the strength in her knees did, too. She sagged against the counter, and the dish she had been drying fell through her trembling fingers back into the sudsy water.

He was compellingly handsome standing there on the last rung of the stairway, his fit body negligently graceful in jeans that fitted tautly over muscled thighs and a shirt unbuttoned to the waist, exposing his broad tanned chest.

"I've been watching you," he admitted, stepping down into the galley and lifting the cover of the ice chest to remove a chilled beer. "Want one?"

The galley seemed to come vitally alive with his presence.

She did want one, but beer aggravated her tendency toward seasickness. "Better not," she replied, acutely conscious of his nearness as he towered behind her, as well as of the difference in him. There was an intensity in his manner tonight that she found disturbing . . . and exciting. She was aware of a tightly reined tension in him.

"You doing okay?" he asked gently.

"Great. Those pills are a life saver."

"Good. There's nothing more awful than being sick on a boat," Race said sympathetically. "Carolyn used to be so sick she'd. . . ." He stopped himself, and when Andrea's face questioned, he said at last in a flat, low tone, not understanding why he said anything. "I was married. Ten years ago. She died." There was pain in his deep voice.

Suddenly she forgot the danger of him.

He felt her hand reach out and touch his shoulder, and he welcomed the light sensation of her fingers.

"Tell me about her, Race," Andrea said very softly, compassion shining in her green eyes. "I would like to know."

He did. He drew her down beside him, and they sat there together in that darkened galley. For the first time in ten years, Race spoke of the woman he had loved and lost. It seemed he talked for hours without stopping. He spoke of private things he never thought he'd speak of to anyone. He told the agony of his heart to a woman he scarcely knew.

"Carolyn was everything to me," he said at last, "wife, lover, best friend, art critic. She went against my family and convinced me to give up my medical practice in favor of what I'd always considered a hobby, my painting. I'd gone into medicine even though I really wanted to paint because my favorite uncle was a small town doctor, and I knew I had to have a profession. I didn't think anyone would take me seriously if I said, 'Look, folks, all I really want to do is paint pictures,' and Uncle Dave seemed to get more out of life than any man I knew. I was too young to realize that was because he was following the path of his heart.

"But Carolyn saw from the first that I'd made a mistake, that I wasn't cut out to be a doctor. She didn't care if the going was rough; she was willing to take the risk. Later, when I became famous and tried to give her some of the credit by pointing out that I never would have done it without her showing me the way, without her selfless willingness to sacrifice a sure thing for my dream, she would always laugh and say, 'Hell, Race, I only pointed out the obvious. You were a damn good artist, and a lousy doctor. Anybody with two eyes in his head could have seen that. And as for being selfless, I was tired of my sleep being interrupted with all those phone calls and you going out in the night and leaving me in that bed by myself. How was I ever going to get pregnant, with you gone all the time?' She wanted a baby so much, but she just couldn't conceive." Race paused, remembering. "When she died, a part of me died, too," he said at last.

For a long moment there was only the swish of the waves and the lulling purr of the engine, but there was a companionable ease between Race and the woman beside him.

"That's how I felt at my parents' funeral, and never a day passes that I don't wish I had them back so I could tell them some little something that has happened to me," Andrea said softly. Her hand was tightly folded in his.

"It may sound trivial, but I was so used to sharing my life with them. There aren't that many people who really care about you. When you lose someone who's very precious, I don't think you ever quite accept their loss. Perhaps if they hadn't been in that accident, I wouldn't have made quite so many mistakes. You see, I married Enrico almost immediately afterward. They had been very set against him, but when they died, and there was no one else . . . and I was—I know this sounds absurd—sort of angry at them for leaving me like that . . . my relationship with him intensified almost at once."

"Maybe you needed the distraction of an Enrico. To get past your grief."

Andrea threw back her head and laughed. The pain of the obsessive Enrico was something she'd largely put behind her.

The velvety sound of her gaiety was a husky pleasure to Race. He liked to hear her laugh, to watch the green of her eyes sparkle as though illuminated with her joy. It brought him back to the present, away from grief and loss as nothing else could.

"Enrico was one hell of a distraction." Andrea chuckled. "He came into my life with the violence of a tornado and ripped me off the solid foundations of my—what do they call it—upwardly mobile, middle class raising. I thought I had to marry him, because I wanted to sleep with him."

She was laughing, her green eyes dancing. The top of her head brushed his cheek, and a sweet perfume rose up from her hair. He was suddenly deeply conscious of her as a woman.

"I'm glad you're no longer so conventional," Race murmured dryly, his hand seeking hers and covering it with a warm kiss. "Maybe that'll come in handy before too long." His tongue flicked over the sudden pulsebeat in her wrist.

The dark eyes that met hers were passionately intense, and for an instant she couldn't draw her gaze from his. She began to tremble. He was joking, but she was afraid of the treacherous, hot feelings even his light jest had so easily aroused.

She yanked her hand from his, wanting to dispel the

force that drew her to him. "I didn't mean that." she snapped, anger flaring at the amusement she saw in his eyes.

He was irritated at himself for disrupting the closeness that had existed between them with that inane, suggestive remark. He supposed he'd done that deliberately in an effort to put distance between them; he remembered too well that she didn't welcome anything that approached lovemaking from him.

Still, when he was with her, despite his efforts not to be, he was always tantalizingly aware of her softness, of her alluring femininity. There was something about Andrea; she had the ability to get too dangerously close to him. "Smooth your ruffled feathers," he chided, reaching for another beer. "I shouldn't have said that. I don't know why I did."

"Probably just to irk me," she pouted, feeling deflated.

"Probably . . ." he said. "But I've done all the talking, and I've probably bored you to tears."

"No, Race. You haven't. I wanted to know about you." It was true. It was terribly important to her to understand him, and she'd been deeply touched by the depth of his love for his wife.

"And I want to know about you," he said huskily. "Tell me about yourself. How did you get into modelling in the first place, and rise above the scrambling thousands of lovelies at the bottom rung of that gilded ladder to fame and fortune?"

She grimaced playfully. "You'd make a good reporter. You know that. That's the first question they always ask. You could read the answer in any one of a dozen magazines."

"Don't brag." he retorted with a jesting wink. "Besides I probably don't subscribe to them. Nor would I want to wade through all the hype if I did. I want the truth. I want to hear every sordid detail of the way you clawed your way to the top, the trampled bodies you had to bury. I want to see blood." He was deliberately distracting her from the private things he'd told her about his relationship with Carolyn.

She laughed merrily. "There wasn't any gore, I can assure you. Enrico put me in a rocket and shot me straight to the top. I was, as they say, an overnight success."

"Good ol' Enrico." Race's voice hardened imperceptibly at the mention of her ex-husband's hand in her success. He was uncomfortably aware of a vague jealousy. "Just how did he do that?"

"I met Enrico shortly before my parents were killed," she began. "It was early fall, and I was an art student at Columbia. I had been given several walks in my classes so I did a very hokey, touristy thing and took the ferry over to see the Statue of Liberty. It was during the middle of the week, so it wasn't very crowded on the island. I set up my easel and began painting."

"Let me guess," Race interrupted, a smile in his voice. "Manhattan held high in the great green lady's right hand, balanced like an overloaded tray that a bad waiter . . ."

Andrea squealed with delight. "You're close! How did you guess?"

"My head in that ball is a recurrent vision."

"The torch was lying somewhere off to the side," Andrea continued, "and it was all wrong. In fact, when Enrico showed up with a gang of models in their far-out clothes I was trying to decide what to do with the torch. Suddenly I decided to put that problem aside and dress the statue in one of the fantastic costumes one of the models was wearing."

"That figures."

"I began sketching the girl's dress. Enrico was screaming and acting just for the world like a grown-up, spoiled brat. I was getting annoyed because of the problem of where to put that torch, and it didn't help when he kept battering at that poor submissive creature who didn't have the backbone of a housefly. I'd always thought a woman as stunning as she could tell any man who looked at her wrong to go to hell. Of course, then I didn't know a thing about models or what they have to endure to keep getting bookings. He could have pulled out a whip and beaten her, and she probably wouldn't have said a word."

Race laughed.

"As I said, I was growing increasingly annoyed."

"I can just see you."

"I've never been able to stand pushy men."

"I know."

"Well, Enrico suddenly did the most outrageous thing."

"What?"

"He stopped in the middle of his very obnoxious tirade and looked over at me as though searching for a means to illustrate some point he was determined to make. I was glaring at him rather fiercely, but he didn't seem to notice. He turned back to the gorgeous housefly and shrieked, 'Why, that blob over there squatting on that stool with the tangled orange mop and the dollop of paint on her impossible nose could be a better model than you.' At first I didn't realize he actually meant me, but when ten submissive, wall-eyed stares began to dissect me, feature by imperfect feature, his meaning sank in. I'd always been overly sensitive about my awkward height and skinniness, and I'm afraid I dressed in baggy clothes hoping that men would think I was modestly concealing alluring curves. They never did, of course."

Race laughed, his intense stare making her skin go hot when his eyes stripped away her clothes. He no longer missed her lack of voluptuous measurements. Instead he admired her softness, her gracefulness, and most of all the tenderness of her heart. "Go on," he murmured softly.

"Well, I saw red, I mean, quite literally, red. I was so mad the Statue of Liberty turned purple. Paint brush in hand I stormed over there and interrupted him in mid-insult. 'Blob!' I screamed. 'The hell you say!' He seemed to see me for the first time, and suddenly I think I really looked at him for the first time. He was very Italian—dark, handsome and, of course, conceited as could be about his looks. He smiled at me, which only made me more furious, but I did notice, as he intended for me to, that when he wasn't yelling, he was quite attractive. 'I am sorry,' he said, oozing charm. 'I quite forgot myself.' He gave the gorgeous girls he'd been berating a much needed break, and took my hand in his, which he held so tightly I couldn't pull it away.

"I wasn't used to men paying attention to me then, and I didn't know how to react. He was looking at me very intently, and I had the uncomfortable feeling he was trying to undress me with his eyes to see if I did have those curves I'd always wished I had. I was used to men doing that, before they looked away. 'You can quit looking at me like that,' I snapped. 'I've always been as skinny as a toothpick and as flat as a French crêpe!'"

Race laughed out loud.

"You can laugh, but it wasn't funny to me in those days. Well, to my stunned surprise Enrico threw back his head and roared with laughter. Unlike all those other men, he did not avert his eyes and look disappointed. 'Miss . . .' he began. When I only stared at him indignantly and refused to supply my name, he went on without it. 'You are the most dynamic woman I have ever met! I want to take pictures of you! I can make you famous and rich and . . . everything else you ever wanted to be.'

" 'I've never wanted to be famous and rich,' I retorted. 'I want to be an artist!'

" 'Nonsense,' he replied. 'That's what everyone wants.'

" 'You must be mad,' I said, letting my eyes wander toward the ferry that was rapidly chugging toward the island, and determining that I'd better pack my easel and run for cover.

" 'No, I'm the great Enrico,' he proclaimed majestically. Race, I stared at him in amazement—I'd never heard of him. My blank look must have at last penetrated his conceit, because he added, 'I'm the most famous fashion photographer in the world.'

"He was painting it on a little thickly, but through the conceit I began to understand that he was for real. The models he had working for him that day were first-class. I still couldn't imagine I could ever be a model; I'd never thought of my looks as anything but a liability. I was tall but not devastatingly gorgeous like the beautiful women he had with him.

" 'But I'm ugly.' I told him. 'I don't look like those girls you're . . .'

" 'You're fascinating,' he told me knowingly. 'Much more interesting to look at than any one of them. Beauty can be very dull.'

"That was the first time I'd ever heard that, but I was growing more conceited by the minute, and more intrigued. I watched him take his pictures that day, and when he was through he took me to dinner at one of the most expensive restaurants in the city. He was so much older, and he knew how to impress a young girl who'd never had any money.

"We began to date, though when he tried to get me to sleep with him, I always said no. He respected me for that I think, more than most men would have because he was Italian, and in the end, I suppose in frustration, he asked me to marry him. All the time he was teaching me things. How to walk, how to talk, how to move and smile, how to use make-up, how to have my hair cut, how to wear clothes. He knew so much. In those days I thought he knew everything. No detail, however small, escaped his attention.

"We'd been married a week. One afternoon he brought home a green velvet dress and some emeralds. He told me to put them on, and he began taking pictures of me. He was very excited, and his excitement infected me. I did outrageous things in front of that camera. He must have taken a thousand pictures before he got one that satisfied him. I didn't know what he intended to do with them. He kept teasing me, saying it would be a surprise.

"I still knew nothing until he and I were standing in front of a newstand in New York and my own face leapt at me from one of the most famous of the fashion magazines. I gasped in amazement. I was so stunningly beautiful that at first I couldn't believe it was really me. In all the fashion sections of the newspapers I began to read that there was a new presence in the fashion industry. Enrico refused to tell anyone who I was for over a month. Reams were written on the mystery woman. Only then did I realize how clever he was, how much he knew not only about photography but the importance of publicity."

Race shifted uneasily, having listened very intently to her story up to this point. "Why did Enrico do all this for you?" he asked at last.

"It was a joke to him, don't you see? That he could take me, a girl, an ugly duckling, he picked up on a lark, and create a star. He hated the big modelling agencies, and I think he did it to put them down. They are the star-makers in the business usually."

"Enrico carried things a little far—for a joke—don't you think?" Race insisted.

"Enrico's very intense. He gets obsessed once he's into a project."

"Obsessed." Race didn't like the word. "And you were a project?"

"One that got out of hand, I'm afraid," Andrea said ruefully. "Though Enrico liked to spend the money I made in very extravagant ways I didn't think we could afford, he didn't like having a wife who was famous. He has a very large ego, and when I didn't obey his every command, he'd fly into rages, screaming that I was nothing before he met me. I would scream back that I never wanted to be a model, that I wanted to paint. And he would yell that I couldn't paint because he knew how that hurt me. We were always in debt, a fact that didn't bother him, but it drove me crazy. Our marriage was on the rocks long before I found him in our bed with one of his models."

"Oh, my God."

"He didn't want to let me go. It was rather difficult, the divorce. He was very possessive, and even though he wasn't faithful and we disagreed about everything, he thought that I belonged to him. Sometimes I think he still does, even though we've become fairly good friends these past few years. He takes me out to dinner almost every week. He still photographs me. I lend him money when he needs it. He made me famous, you know, and he doesn't ever let me forget that."

"But you didn't want to be rich and famous," Race said with deep understanding. "You wanted to paint."

"I don't think I can now. I've wasted too much time on other things."

Race was looking at her strangely, his dark eyes glowing and intense. "It's very easy, really," he said softly, taking her hand in his and playing with her fingers.

She was instantly aware of his physical contact.

"All you have to do is make a commitment with your heart," he said. For an instant she caught her breath as he stared deeply into her eyes. "In Texas I'll show you how."

His expression was so warm, and she sensed a new closeness to him because of the confidences they'd shared, a closeness that only made her attraction to him all the more dangerous. Theirs was a love that could never be.

Race felt it too. Suddenly he had to touch her and hold her, despite his rational misgivings. In the darkness his lips were seeking hers.

She knew she should run away. It was dangerous to stay with him in their present mood. But she could only stare up at him transfixed, paralyzed by a force stronger than her conscious will. His hands were suddenly heavy on her shoulders, preventing her escape. Long fingers moved caressingly along the nape of her neck, and a brilliant spray of tingling fire shot through her as she tried, too late, to pull away. Then he drew his arms down and tightened them around her small body, crushing her breasts against the solid wall of his chest.

"God, you're beautiful," he groaned.

She parted her lips, letting her tongue flick over their softness to moisten them in anticipation of his descending mouth.

She closed her eyes, thinking only of the way his lips felt, the delicious taste of them, the way his tongue felt against hers as it slid against her teeth deeply into her mouth. She was exhilarated by every delicate sensation, by the hardness of his arms around her, by the overwhelming size of his powerfully masculine body pressing intimately against hers. She tasted the faintest traces of beer in his mouth, savored the musky maleness of his flesh. A bewildering tide of intense desire swept her, and the will to resist needs long denied seeped out of her. She wanted him. She'd gone too long without a man to talk to, to confide in, to be close to, a man to make love to. To love.

"Oh, Race," she sighed softly, yielding in wanton, flaming surrender. She leaned her bright head against his chest, covering his shoulders with the thick red softness of her curls. Her hands moved over him, sliding beneath his shirt to caress the warmth of his flesh. He felt so good, and her fingers moved lower, slipping between the waistband of his jeans to caress his lower belly, to explore his manliness. "Oh, Race . . ." she breathlessly murmured again, deliberate invitation in her husky voice.

Suddenly he wrenched himself away, seizing her tiny hands in his, removing tantalizing fingers from himself before he went mad with his own need for her. His features were hard.

"Race. What?" she murmured dazedly. "Why not?"

Slowly her long silken lashes fluttered open and she became conscious of his harsh expression. "What's wrong? I don't understand."

"Don't you?" he muttered grimly. For a moment he'd almost forgotten himself. "Three nights ago you explained your feelings. Maybe I have my own reasons for not wanting to get involved with you."

His words were like a cold wave drowning the fire of her blazing emotions as she remembered how deliberately remote he'd been since that morning he'd left her in bed.

She stared helplessly up at him, feeling more thoroughly confused than ever. She wanted Race, but she loved Don—didn't she? Had the world gone crazy? Or had she? She reached out for him, but he captured her trembling fingers before she could touch him.

"You'll thank me tomorrow," he said heavily.

The flush in her cheeks was suddenly as brilliant as

the color of her hair. Her eyes blazed with the hurt of his rejection. She ached shamelessly with frustration. At that moment she almost hated him as well as herself.

"Go away," she cried miserably, her feminine pride in shreds. "Just go away." She stared wretchedly down at her shaking hands, hating them, too, because they betrayed the intensity of her womanly needs; when she looked up, she saw he was gone.

She felt strangely desolate. This was what she wanted —what she'd told him she wanted, she reminded herself as a salve to her wounded pride—and he'd given it to her with insulting ease.

She chewed the swollen softness of her bottom lip until it was tender with pain. What was it that she wanted? She was so confused. She'd wanted him to kiss her, but she needed so much more than his kisses. But it was too soon for that. He was Don's brother. Race had a life she knew nothing about—*his own reasons,* he had said, for not wanting to get involved. Did they include other women? At this thought an inexplicable shaft of pure pain shot through her. Perhaps there was only one woman. She stared blindly before her, the pain in her heart even worse. Logic told her that a man like Race would never live without women in his life. He'd invited her to come with him to Texas only because of his sense of family responsibility. Race was simply picking up the pieces of a messy relationship Don had inflicted upon him. Undoubtedly, Race was being kind to her for the same reason. This last was the most miserable thought of all.

Perhaps because her mood was so bleak, the motion of the boat began to bother her even more than usual. Weakly she arose and poured water into a paper cup, and swallowed two more pills. Much later, when she went to bed that night she swallowed her last Dramamine tablet.

"Oh, Lord," she cried into her wadded pillow. She felt her heart was tied in a knot that was more savagely painful than the knots in her stomach.

What was she going to do? She didn't know herself anymore. She felt as frightened, as unsure, as a lost child.

Chapter 7

THE NEXT MORNING ANDREA AWOKE QUITE LATE. THE thick, unpleasant odor of frying bacon came to her nostrils, and she knew instantly that Felix had assumed her duties in the galley. The smell seemed to choke her like a noxious gas, and she lay back in her bed, feeling hot and queasy, a faint sheen of perspiration glowing on her pale skin. She pushed her face against the cool sheet until it was in the direct path of the air sifting through the windows.

Outside the portholes she could see that the sun was already high in a white sky. The heat seemed hotter than it ever had, the breeze flowing past her face was heavy and sticky. Just then, the roilings of her stomach nearly overcame her, and she had to climb weakly from her bed and rush to the boat's "head".

Later she collapsed in the bathroom, her damp head lying against the cold fibreglass floor. She didn't know how long she lay there, weakly bathing her face with a cool rag, but she couldn't bring herself to get up because the coolness of the floor against her hot cheek was so soothing. Silently she cursed herself for being so weak, and then she cursed the waves and the rocking boat and Race and Don and then every circumstance in her life that had compelled her presence on this boat.

She lay there for a long time, her thoughts a violent, irrational muddle, before she heard several harsh knocks against her door. "Oh, dear . . ." she moaned as she groped for a handrail to pull herself up with. Then, more loudly, "Coming."

She had barely stumbled to her knees when Race barged inside. His dark features were so forbiddingly cold she shrank back against the floor.

When he saw her, his tanned face went as white as hers.

"Andrea! My God. What's the matter?"

His horrified expression was hardly flattering.

"I'm okay, Race." Her voice was a tiny, thin sound, so unlike her own that she knew it did little to instill confidence in him. She tried to smile, but from his expression, the grimace she managed was obviously no more reassuring.

He knelt beside her, his strong arms lifting her against her body, his countenance grave. He felt the lightness of her, the clammy perspiration of her skin. She was as weak as a kitten.

"Hell, Andrea, you're practically wasting away. You were already too thin, but if we weren't within twenty-four hours of Galveston, I'd be frantic."

"Twenty-four hours . . . that long?" she groaned, sinking against his strong body. "I ran out of those pills you gave me. Last night," she whispered.

"Why didn't you tell me then?" he asked gently. "I could have found something else."

"I didn't think you had anything else. I didn't want to bother you."

"No . . ." he muttered, unable to keep a trace of sarcasm from edging his deep tone. "That's not dramatic enough to be your style. You'd rather I found you collapsed on the floor."

"I didn't think."

"I'm beginning to wonder if you ever do."

Andrea trembled violently, and he regretted his harshness. She was too unsteady to endure his anger, no matter how justified.

Carefully, he swung her up into his arms and carried her back to his bed. "I guess this is one time I don't have to tell you to stay put," he said with a gentler tone. He smoothed her hair back against the pillow and bathed her hot face with the damp rag.

She managed a faint smile, and said dimly, "No."

He left her, returning a few minutes later with several packets of pills. His expression was still grave. "Andrea, I don't want you gobbling these like candy the way you must have with the Dramamine. I don't like this drug nearly as well. In fact, I can't remember now why I even have it on board. Since it's packaged in these samples for doctors, I can only assume one of my doctor friends gave them to me."

His manner was so stern that Andrea grew alarmed. "What's the matter with these pills?"

"This drug, if taken in a large enough dose, can occasionally have a side effect I don't like," he explained. "Something we call twilight sleep. A patient can do things without remembering later that he did them."

"Is that all?" Andrea cracked open a package. So what if she forgot something she did. Anything was better than lying for hours on that bathroom floor, suffering contorted agonies that very much resembled those of a dying fish that had recklessly flipped out of the water onto the beach.

"Just be careful," Race warned.

"Don't worry," she replied, her expression so sweetly obedient he would have been alarmed had he noted it. "I'll follow the directions on the package exactly." She intended to, of course.

"Good."

He left her only when he saw that some of her color had returned.

Thirty minutes later she was feeling enough better to get out of bed and dress.

As the day passed, Race's warning faded in her memory. The drug greatly helped her, even though she took more of them than perhaps she should have.

Despite her attempts to show Race her gratitude in small ways, he coolly rebuffed her. Last night, when they'd been talking to one another, a closeness had grown between them, but it was a closeness Race obviously regretted, for reasons Andrea could not fully understand.

"Leave it alone," she kept telling herself, but it seemed impossible for her not to think of Race. He was becoming a most unwelcome obsession, but perhaps that was because on a boat there wasn't all that much to do.

Every time she chanced to find herself in his company, she was extremely aware of his handsomeness, of a queer stirring deep within her. Then she would remember his rejection the night before and proudly attempt to behave disdainfully herself. Always when she acted haughty, his demeanor turned even colder.

Because of the heat, Race had stripped to the waist. Though she tried to draw her gaze away, when he wasn't looking at her she found herself letting her eyes roam over his bronzed physique. With much interest.

He was superbly made, the female in her noted, like some wild, grand jungle animal. Long brown muscles magnificently conditioned, his stomach flat and hard, his hips narrow. She loved the darkness of him; she'd never been able to tan and had to avoid the sun.

More than a little disturbed by the way just the mere sight of him evoked a disturbing warmness in her, she tried to occupy herself with other things. But she found difficulty doing so. Her fingers shook when she tried to mend a shirt she'd torn. Their trembling became so pronounced she couldn't even thread her needle, and she gave up, sighing in frustration. She burnt two dishes in the kitchen, and she couldn't concentrate on any of the magazines she tried to read.

As the long hot day wore away, hour by tedious hour, she grew increasingly edgy. He, on the other hand, seemed happy enough to avoid her, sketching with an intensity of interest that maddened her even as she envied him his ability to do so.

That evening, Race took his supper alone at the wheel, and she was left with the dour Felix for company. Jake was asleep, readying himself to take the wheel during the nightwatch.

Feeling rejected and disconsolate, Andrea went to bed early herself, taking one of the pills Race had given her. It wasn't long before a drugged drowsiness overcame her, and she fell into a deep sleep.

Even in her sleep, visions of Race plagued her, and her dreams were hotly erotic. The drug she'd swallowed seemed to sing in her veins, and her body glowed with the kindling heat of desire. The soft rocking movements lulled her, the sea breezes drifting into the room cooled her warm body. Because of the heat she wore only a thin cotton t-shirt that barely covered her thighs. The long length of her graceful legs were exposed to the cool air wafting into the room.

In her dreams Race was with her, holding her, caressing her, tenderly possessing her. She moaned his name in a passionate whisper, "Race."

"Hmmm." The deep, amused sound was so real, it jarred her senses.

Her eyelids fluttered drowsily in languid confusion when she saw him standing in the middle of the room. A shaft of moonlight touched his handsome face and broad shoulders. His smooth, brown skin gleamed in the silvery light, and then she drifted back to sleep, a soft smile of arousal illuminating her face.

Vaguely she felt the warmth of his palm on her brow, and as he was drawing the sheet to cover her bare legs, she reached up and took his hand in hers, bringing it to her lips and kissing it as she had been doing in her dreams.

Race groaned aloud at the heat of her lips on his flesh. Did she think him made of stone—immune to her beauty, immune to her feminine warmth? All day he'd sought to avoid her. He gazed down at her, seeing bright, softly curling hair flowing across the pillow of his bed, seeing her sweet face flushed with desire, and he wanted her with an intensity that tortured him. He could not stop himself from imagining—and remembering—how those full lips that kissed the insides of his fingers with passion would feel beneath his mouth, how her warm silken body would curve to fit his.

He had to get out of here, away from her at once. He'd only come in to check on her and make sure that she was all right, since Felix had told him that she'd been unusually quiet during supper and had returned earlier than usual to bed. He'd thought she was ill.

He tried to withdraw his hand, but she wouldn't let him leave. She clasped him tightly, and then he felt her tongue again moisten the skin between his fingers. She slid her other hand across the broad expanse of his chest, twining her pale fingers into the mat of black hair that covered his bronzed skin. This deliberate, wanton touching created a surge of electricity charging from her to him, obliterating his will to leave.

Did she have any idea what she was doing to him?

All day he'd told himself fiercely that he was satisfied with his life exactly as it was. Long ago he'd loved and lost, almost losing his soul in his unbearable grief. For ten years he'd been shackled by no woman. He had a relationship that satisfied his needs, a woman who understood him and made no demands. He did not want to change either himself or his comfortable lifestyle.

But when Andrea's slight arms curved around his muscled neck they would have been powerless to draw his head down had he not willingly obliged.

Andrea kissed him then; deeply, provocatively, letting her trembling lips meld with his, opening her mouth so that his tongue could slide inside to her molten inner depths.

The moment his hard mouth touched the exquisite softness of hers, he knew he was lost. Her hands began moving lightly over his body, touching him everywhere, immodestly learning every secret of his body, exploring him intimately. He felt thoroughly aroused. Never had he been more so. There was an excitingly wanton boldness in this woman that he'd never known in another.

Desire overcame him, and he broke into a hot sweat. He could scarcely think because of the hot lips urgently mating with his, the warm hands caressing him. Still, he had to give her one more chance.

"You don't really want this," he mumbled against her seductive lips. "Tomorrow you'll hate me, as well as yourself."

"No," she murmured, feeling faint and weak with needs that she understood no better than he. "I won't hate you, Race. I could never hate you. I want to be yours."

She was past thought—past reason, and, he realized, so was he. His mouth met hers again, and desire consumed him. "To hell with tomorrow," he thought fleetingly. This was the twentieth century. She was a modern woman. She'd been married. Doubtless she'd had innumerable affairs. Why couldn't he take her without owing her anything of himself?

Only feeling mattered, only the erotic movements of her hands on his flesh, her lips worshipping him with the hot ardor of her molten kisses, her mouth lingering and seeking, moving downward from his lips over his body, discovering mysterious erogenous zones, until his breath came in harsh gasps.

For a moment Race drew away so he could strip quickly out of his jeans. She watched him, fascinated. In the darkness she thought him magnificent. A sun-bronzed giant of a man with silver moonlight gleaming on his wide shoulders and chest and taut stomach. His long muscled legs were planted slightly apart as he stood over her, staring down at her. Then the bunk dipped beneath his weight as he sat gently on its edge. Slowly, he reached toward her and lifted her shirt from her body, removing it slowly, inch by inch, so as to savor the provocative exposure of her loveliness completely.

She slipped trembling velvet fingers behind his neck and drew him down to her. Her skin was vibrantly warm where it touched his, the scent of her a heady aphrodisiac that intoxicated him, aroused him, stimulating every sense.

She smiled softly, and her gentle face had never seemed more beautiful to him, the sensual message in her brilliant eyes never more inticingly seductive.

He almost feared he was in a dream that would

disappear when he tried to make her his. But the soft, vital flesh enveloping him was very real.

How he wanted her. His need flowed through him like fire.

Her breath whispered in his ear. "Race, my darling. I love you so."

Love. Just for a moment he drew back, startled by the depth of sincerity he heard in the husky sound, stunned by the overpowering need in his own reaction.

"I am yours, my darling," she murmured, "for always."

Her soft arms circled his neck, and she drew his face down to hers. His eyes swept her body in a long, passionate caress. His blood surged in a violent rush as every male sense filled with her voluptuous presence.

Then his mouth eagerly possessed hers, and she moaned softly beneath his fevered kisses, from the hot sensations he aroused with his exploring, expert hands.

He was so large, his massive body hovering over hers. The strangeness of him excited her as his flesh slid warmly against hers, the motion of the boat rocking their bodies in a wanton, liquid dance like a slow, erotic cradle. He pressed her beneath him deeply into the sheets, shifting his body over hers, exploring, seeking that yielding secret part of that which was waiting to welcome him. She felt warm, incredibly tight. He rejoiced in the wildly savage, pagan splendor of his ultimate possession.

For a long time he forced himself not to move on her, savoring that first moment of the warm union of their flesh, with her body opening to his like a soft new blossom unfolding its delicate petals, sensing how special she would always be to him.

The boat rocked the lovers gently and, despite Race's deliberate stillness, the rhythmic motions sent their passions soaring, building like a stormy thunder-

head billowing explosively toward the heavens. His lips
tenderly kissed her eyelids, tantalizing her with gentle,
light kisses, when she wanted him to plunder her mouth
with urgent kisses, when she wanted him to take her
deeply, violently, shatteringly.

She arched her body wantonly beneath him, and her
movement sent a splintering shaft of desire shuddering
through him. He drew a ragged breath, pausing in his
kisses. Again she moved, trying to force him to completion, but the second time he only smiled, both amused
and flattered by her impatience.

"Be patient, little one," he murmured, for the moment, in perfect, triumphant control of his masculine
passion. "We have the rest of the night." The rest of
our lives. . . ." The thought was hazy, forgotten in the
passionate turmoil of his emotions.

He eased his body from hers, and when she cried out
in hungry frustration, her body wracked from the
unexpected loss, he silenced her with a scorching kiss.
When he at last felt her protests ebb to no more than a
gutteral groan deep within her throat, his lips moved
lower once again to her breasts where he nibbled and
sucked the hardened pink crests of delight, moving
leisurely from the small fullness of one pulsating bosom
to the other, before he let his mouth and tongue roam
still lower, past the shadowy indentation of her navel,
to the warm, erotically hot, love-sweetened heart of
her desire.

"No," she thought in vague but wantonly pleasured
embarrassment, it was too soon between them for that.
He wasn't going to kiss her there. . . .

But he was.

She tried to twist away from this ultimate intimacy
with his mouth, this ultimate intimacy with him, but his
hands hardened on her soft body, and he held her still,
effortlessly, so his hard lips could ravage the exquisitely
voluptuous softness of her femininity.

He wanted her as he'd never wanted any woman, and he wanted to pleasure her as she'd never been pleasured before.

Deep in a corner of his mind he registered that this slender woman, despite her lack of voluptuous flesh, was an intensely sexual creature, much more so than many of the more beautiful women he'd known. He sensed her desire for him was a craving hunger, a desperate need linked to her heart.

He bent his head to his purpose. The moisture of his mouth was an invasion of liquid flame that poured from him to her. His lips and expert hands practiced the most sensitive sorcery, and Andrea began to glow to the sensuous throbbing between her creamy thighs, utterly powerless to resist his ravishment.

He lazily toyed with her, the touch of his mouth silken. Her softest flesh was pliant beneath his hard kisses and the more delicate manipulations of his tongue. She quivered with his every hot breath, with his light, kneading caresses.

Andrea moaned as his mouth teased her to the very edge of excruciating pleasure. Then, at last she had to cover her face with a pillow to stifle her scream of sensual release as wave after wave of white-hot fire rent her body like a shaft of lightning as her passions exploded in a long ripple of carnal sensation that left her limp and weak and shuddering.

Sweet love flowed out of her, enveloping him as his hands gripped her softly rounded hips, his tongue thrusting even more deeply. She screamed again and again into the smothering softness as her body quivered and pulsated against his skillful plundering lips.

At last he drew away, shifting his thoroughly roused body in one decisive movement to take her as she'd begged him to before. He felt desperate for relief as he fitted himself on top of her, crushing her breasts beneath the weight of his chest; he buried his hot face

in her hair, against the warm damp flesh of her throat.
Her hands were in his hair and then tracing a path down
the sensitive line of his spine while she murmured his
name. She buried her lips against his neck. He felt the
wanton movement of her body as she urged him
seductively toward his own pulsing completion. He
took her then with all the shattering force she'd desired, and a fresh shocking geyser of pleasure burst
through her, and then another and another, until she
could only cling to him, her whole body spent and
shivering, her soul, though she did not know it, lost to
him in the process.

Chapter 8

ANDREA AND RACE WERE STILL, SAVE FOR THEIR FAINT,
irregularly drawn breaths. A gentle breeze gusted over
their hot bodies, cooling them as they relaxed in
silence.

Race lay back, the deepest emotions of his heart a
turmoil. He was astounded at what had taken place, his
mind incapable of rationally explaining the deep sexual
accord of their bodies. It was ironic that six days ago
he'd looked at Andrea and thought her skinny and tall
and unappealing, not his sort of woman at all. He'd
considered the fashion industry insane to choose her as
its reigning queen. What was it that he'd said to
himself, when he'd gotten his first really good look of
her in that white slip or whatever it was that had left
nothing to the imagination? "Damned fools all of them.
They don't know what the hell a good-looking woman is
supposed to look like. All she is is a human hanger for
idiotically designed fashions real women can't wear any-

way." He'd actually been pleased to discover Andrea so undesirable, since that would make his task of turning Don's interest from her all the easier.

Undesirable. He was the one who was the fool. He'd thought large breasts and swaying hips made a woman, rather than her heart and soul. He had been blinded by a woman's outward appearances so long he'd never bothered to look beneath the surface, telling himself there was no need, because his taste in women was strictly governed by their appearance. Andrea had forced him to see her as a person.

Like all the other women in his life, Carolyn had been dark and small and beautiful with voluptuous breasts and hips. He'd been so captivated by her beauty he hadn't discovered the brash sweetness of her personality for months. How many times had she taunted him that if she hadn't had the looks of a movie starlet, he would never have stayed around long enough to realize she had a brain too.

Andrea was the first woman who'd instantly forced him out of this mold. Now Race saw her as a wanton siren who'd woven a spell upon him that seemed to grow more powerful with the passing of each day.

Deeply as he had loved Carolyn, it had taken them years to achieve the same degree of harmony in bed he'd discovered on his first night with Andrea. By that time, Carolyn and he had been lovers for such a long time, that their passion, deeply satisfying as it had been, had lacked the spice of novelty he'd enjoyed with Andrea tonight.

Why?

Was it only that Andrea had appeared at an extremely unlikely place at a damnably convenient time—alone on a boat, away from all other women? Once he was home, with Rebecca, would he view this time with Andrea as no more than a bizarre interlude with an exotically different kind of woman, the sowing of a few last oats before he settled himself again into marriage with the kind of woman he knew how to manage?

In the glimmering half-light Andrea stretched languidly, moonlight covering her slim body like a shimmering, transparent veil. She shifted, feeling the luxuriant warmth of Race's powerful body beside her.

For once in her life she'd gotten exactly what she wanted and been completely satisfied, she thought dazedly. Had she been a cat, she would have purred. As it was, she sighed blissfully, and snuggled against the lean hot body, deeply, happily aware of his maleness.

She leaned toward him and traced the curve of his roughened cheek.

"Race?"

"Hmmm?"

"I . . . want to kiss . . . you," she said hesitantly, a bold, hot glimmer lighting those bewitching eyes of hers, as one of her hands closed over him in such an intimate caress that he caught a sharp, ragged breath.

At first her meaning didn't penetrate. Then it went through him like electricity. Abruptly his attention was turned from his vague musings to the erotic mystery of the smiling woman beside him, to the wanton movement of her fingers lightly circling him. Desire swelled in him instantly. He was rawly alert in the space of a second.

It was with the greatest difficulty that he pulled himself away from the steady, rhythmic pleasure of her moving hands.

"I think I'll shower first," he said. "It feels like a furnace in here." Never in all his life had he felt so hot.

"Perhaps," she said, a smile in her voice, "I can kiss you while you shower."

Kiss. He was beginning to like her rather liberal definition of that word.

"I see you have a talent for compromise besides your
other . . . quite remarkable talents," he said aloud.
Then his lips sought her and he drew her body hard
down upon his own so he could kiss her deeply.

In the shower, cool water splashed over their bodies,
rivulets streaming down his massive chest and narrow
waist into the silken tangle of her red curls as she knelt
before him, massaging her face lovingly, tentatively,
shyly against his hardened manhood. At that first
lightest touch of her lips, he groaned.

She had no doubt about the rightness of what she
did. It seemed almost sacred, her loving him. Some
feeling of closeness that she did not understand bound
her to this man, made the intimacies of love-making
with him the most natural, the most wonderful experience in the world. Her gentle fingertips traced over
every masculine part of his body, delicately, little
imagining the splintering, piercing sensations they
aroused.

She felt his hands in her thick wet hair, holding her
close against him, moving her head against himself. He
was staring down at her as the warm stream of water
flowed over his body to hers, watching her, loving her.

She glowed, radiant with the softest emotion she'd
ever felt. She wanted to give him pleasure as he had
given her, to tell him with her lips the depth of the
passions in her soul. She wanted to know him, to
belong to him. And she wanted him to belong to her.

At that, he moved away, his body taut and feverish
with explosive passions. Gently he lifted her up to him,
and then urgently pressed her against the cool fibreglass
of the shower wall, and encased himself in the hot living
blossom of her tenderest flesh.

She felt his great body shaking. His passion excited
her, and she clung breathlessly to him, surrendering her
lips to his warm mouth, arching her body for the
explosive tide of his passion's release as her hands

tightly clasped his lean hard hips in an effort to pull him even closer to her. The flame of his desire erupted in him and spread like a conflagration through her, as for one blazing moment of timeless splendor they came together, two melting into one, shedding their self-control and losing themselves one in the other.

Slowly Race fell back into himself. He felt the feeble trickle of warm water scalding the length of his spine, and he reached up and turned the water off.

"You know what we just did?" His low, warm chuckle vibrated against her skin.

She shook her head, not understanding.

"We just ran out every gallon of fresh water in our reserve tank."

"Oh."

He cupped her chin gently. "But it was worth it."

Then his mouth closed over hers.

When Andrea awoke, shafts of white light were streaming inside the stateroom despite the fact that someone had thoughtfully pulled the curtains together. Andrea lay still, savoring the difference in the boat and in herself. She felt so thoroughly rested and refreshed, so deeply contented.

At first she did not understand. The air in the cabin was cooler than usual, dryer. The outside sounds muted, the roar of the engine . . .

There was no roar of the engine.

The boat was strangely still, and in a flash she realized that some time in the night they must have docked. Odd that she had no memory of it.

Or had they reached Galveston the day before? As she mulled the matter over she realized that her memory of yesterday was unusually hazy. She couldn't remember a thing that had happened after that nap she'd taken in the afternoon.

Not a thing.

A shockwave of fear shot through her as she struggled fiercely to concentrate, but without successfully remembering anything. Those hours were wiped from her mind as though her brain were a slate that had been thoroughly scrubbed. Nothing . . . not a fragment came back to her.

Vaguely Andrea remembered Race's misgivings about the pills he'd given her for her seasickness. Perhaps she had taken one or two more than she had needed. Hadn't he said that in some people they produced a kind of amnesia, that one could behave in a perfectly rational manner, and yet later not remember a thing that had happened?

She would have to ask Race about it, she decided, about what she'd done during those lost hours, she was extremely curious. Once, she'd had a friend with a drinking problem who always suffered a memory loss if she had more than four or five drinks. Elaine had always wanted to know everything, even the most insignificant details about what she'd done. Andrea now understood her friend better than she ever had before.

There was something deeply disturbing about the prospect of having done things without remembering them. It felt as if another person had inhabited her body while she slept. At least, she consoled herself, unlike her Elaine, she hadn't been drunk, and she wouldn't have to suffer any embarrassment over having behaved irresponsibly or having done anything she might regret.

Andrea slipped from the bed, shivering in the air-conditioning. Her body felt . . . she couldn't quite put her finger on it. What was it? . . . Just different . . . She supposed this to be from the lingering effect of that drug. Well, thank Heavens she wouldn't have to worry about seasickness any more, and there would be no necessity to take strange drugs that affected one's memory and one's body.

When her feet touched the carpet she saw a brown rectangular object peeping from beneath the corner of the bunk. Curious, she reached down for it, and several snapshots fluttered to the floor from a man's wallet. She picked up the pictures, one by one, realizing that they must belong to Race. She hated the curiosity that drove her to study each picture, but she wanted to know about him.

Two of them were old and faded and she supposed they must be his mother and father. There was one of Don and Linda and two golden children that looked exactly alike. Two children. Twins. They were so beautiful, their innocent young faces bringing it home to Andrea how very married Don was, how close to disaster she'd almost come by involving herself with him. Strangely, she felt nothing except the most intense relief. She was numb, she guessed.

The last picture was of a dazzlingly beautiful woman with dark curling hair and softly pretty features. She had a bustline that made Andrea turn green, and she quickly flipped the picture to spare herself the agony of comparison and read the writing on the back.

The inscription was simple but meaningful: "Love, Rebecca." Andrea could tell by the date that the photograph was a recent one.

Trembling fingers slid the picture back into the wallet, and Andrea folded the wallet without knowing that she did so. She sank back against the bunk, the wallet still clutched in her hand, close to her heart.

Andrea's face grew pale. Her vision blurred, and she blinked hard, wondering why her stomach suddenly felt so hollow.

The girl could be anyone, of course, but Andrea's feminine instinct told her that the woman must be very special to Race for him to keep her picture with the others that were so obviously members of his family.

Slowly Andrea remembered Race's rejection of her two nights before. She'd been shamelessly willing, and he'd been the one to draw away. Yesterday, she remembered, he'd avoided her. Clearly he did not want to become more than casually involved with her, as she did not rationally want to with him. And he was trying to let her know this in a kind way.

Andrea was beginning to realize that her feelings for Race ran too deep to be easily rationalized. How had things gone so far, so quickly?

At first all she'd seen was that he was a virile and handsome man, that her heart always beat faster when he came near her. But gradually the force of his personality had become his predominantly compelling attraction, drawing her to him with even more power than his good looks.

It was only natural that she should like him. He was charming and intelligent, sensitive to her feelings. He'd put himself to a great deal of trouble at her expense. He'd been so kind when he'd told her about Don and talked to her afterward. Then he'd saved her life, at very real risk to his own. How cheerfully he'd saddled himself with a weak, easily nauseated creature on his yacht for days. He'd given up his own comfortable bed so she could enjoy it. All these things he'd done for her, and she'd done little for him in return.

He'd even gone so far as to invite her to Texas out of a sense of family obligation toward his brother. He'd understood her devastation because of Don, and he wanted to take care of her until she was strong enough to cope.

He was exactly the kind of man she'd longed to meet and fall in love with. In the beginning she'd believed Enrico to be his sort. He was, in short, the man she'd believed Don to be.

Andrea stared blindly about the stateroom, the vision of the lovely Rebecca haunting her. She had no right to care this much, so soon. She'd known him less than a week. But she was beginning to realize it was a week unlike any other in her life.

She was falling in love with him. But that was impossible. There was Don. Strange that she could scarcely summon the image of his golden face. Funny how little he seemed to matter. Had he only been a dream that she in her desperate loneliness had fought very hard to believe in?

Oh, my God, she wailed inwardly. She'd heard of the danger of falling in love on the rebound, but she'd never experienced it before. How, how could she be feeling like this? It made no sense. A few days with Race. That's all they'd had. But being on a boat with someone, sharing moments of intense closeness, being cut off from all other distractions, was a kind of concentrated experience. It was like putting time in a capsule and strengthening its power. It didn't take nearly so long to develop a relationship with a person when you lived with him day and night with nothing else to focus your attention upon.

Pushing her thoughts of Race aside, she forced herself to get dressed. Her hair was unusually tangled, and she had to pull the brush through it nearly a hundred times before it spilled smoothly over her shoulders once again in gleaming, coiling tresses. It smelled sweet, too, as though she'd washed it.

In the mirror her face was strangely radiant. Much more beautiful than usual.

"Ah, well," she sighed, slipping into Jake's jeans, "Being near firm, unteetering land obviously agrees with me."

When she went topside she saw the three men were busy, hosing the boat, lifting heavy containers to and from the dock. Race was ashore talking to several men she didn't know. When she caught sight of him, a strange, desperate breathlessness seized her, and she did not call out to him. Remembering his coolness from yesterday, and newly aware of the astounding depth of her own feelings for him, she decided it was best for them both if she avoided him.

It was a way of hiding, she supposed, as she headed back down the stairs. She felt that if she saw him, he would see the secrets of her heart as clearly as though she had held it in the open palm of her hand and given it to him. There was fear in opening herself to him, fear in trying to trust again, fear in letting him come close enough to see all the little faults that she was so much more comfortable concealing.

She went into the galley and began cleaning it up, stowing the necessary supplies neatly in the cabinets, keeping herself busy to avoid thought.

She heard a man's swift tread descending the stairs, and when she turned, her eyes met the intense, electric blackness of Race's gaze. Why was he looking at her like that, as though he searched for her soul?

She went warm suddenly, despite the air-conditioning in the galley. In such close quarters, it was impossible to ignore the man's sensuous masculinity.

She turned away so he wouldn't see the flame color of her cheeks, wishing, too, that she could cast off the powerful spell of his vital sensuality.

"Aren't you speaking to people this morning?" he asked quietly from behind her, sensing her fear of him and not liking it. "I saw you on deck a while ago."

"Oh, hello," she said with a deliberate air of indifference, brushing back a strand of red hair that had fallen into her eyes, keeping her face averted, all the time feeling more crazily mixed up than she ever had in her life. "Would you like a cup of coffee?" she managed at last in a distraught mumble.

"Coffee." His mind exploded in surprise and masculine hurt. Did she really think he'd come down for that?

"Well. I know I slept late, and I didn't know if you'd already had any."

"I haven't. No one has as a matter of fact, because . . ." He stopped, suddenly, his smile broadening into a warm, appealing grin despite himself.

"Oh. Then I'll make some," she said, unaware of the grin, not understanding the sudden warmth in his voice.

Race's expression hardened again at her casual tone. He stared at her in stunned amazement, not liking her nonchalant manner, her deliberate attempt at sophisticated indifference, her determination to avoid even looking at him. When he remembered her warmth of last night, her bold invitation to him that she join him in bed, he couldn't understand her coolness this morning. What sort of woman was she? he wondered cynically. Were nights like last night so commonplace to her they meant absolutely nothing? Or was she regretting what had happened? He stared at her, not liking either thought.

She tried to flip on the fresh water to fill the coffee pot, but no water came out, only a rush of air. "Oh, dear," she muttered, glancing toward Race's darkening features, feeling more uncomfortable than ever that he seemed to be growing angry for some unfathomable reason. "There's no water."

"No, there isn't." Again there was warmth in his low tone. This time she saw his grin, and it made her go hot all over. "A small price to pay."

"For what?" she stared up at him, questioningly, innocently, her emerald eyes blank. "I don't know what you're talking about."

Something in her manner brought him sharply to attention. He'd been on the verge of coming toward her, of trying to right the wrongness between them, but he stopped right where he was and stared at her hard as though there were something about her he didn't understand. His sharp scrutiny was making her very uncomfortable.

"Race, are you all right?"

"Perfectly," he replied, but his low-timbred voice was no longer so gentle. A disturbing thought had formed in his mind.

To her he seemed restless suddenly and very ill at ease. "You're acting so strange," she said, feeling more thoroughly confused than ever.

"Am I? Then you really don't remember—why we ran out of water?"

"No." She didn't relish admitting that she didn't remember a thing, especially since he'd warned her so implicitly yesterday morning, and today he seemed to be in such a bad mood. "I went to bed so early . . ." she evaded.

But he wouldn't let her evade. "You took a shower," he persisted.

She only stared at him in confusion. Had she? That must have been when she'd washed her hair. "Did I leave the water on?" she asked in a small, frightened voice. He was looking at her so oddly that her heart began to pound with fear. She sensed that something was dreadfully wrong. "Oh, Race, I'm sorry. Is that why you're mad at me this morning? I can't believe I was so thoughtless. It must have happened because I was so very tired, don't you see?"

Race scowled more deeply, his expression belying his next words. "I'm not mad at you, damn it. I'm . . . I'm . . ." He slammed his hand against the panelled wall, and a pain shot from his wrist up the length of his arm. If he wasn't mad, what the hell was he then? Frustrated as hell, for one thing, feeling soft toward a woman that didn't care about him at all. In a damned impossible tight spot for another. The little

fool had obviously taken too much of that Scopola-
mine. But as he remembered how terribly seasick she'd
been, he couldn't blame her for that.

How could he tell her about last night, that she'd
invited him into her bed? From her cool manner this
morning, he could only interpret that she would be
deeply ashamed and upset by what had happened.
There was no way he could really make her understand.
Doubtless, she would blame him for taking advantage
of her, for giving her the medicine in the first place. Just
as he was already beginning to blame himself. He'd
been a doctor too long to shirk his responsibility in the
affair.

What had she said that first morning on the boat
when she'd shared his bed? That she'd only be using
him if they had sex, that the man she was in love with
was his brother. She hadn't wanted last night, and she
would be deeply ashamed if he told her.

Why hadn't he thought last night? But she'd behaved
so rationally, a little drowsily perhaps, but she'd been
herself. Now, belatedly, he wondered about birth
control. He'd been so sure that she knew what she was
doing, he hadn't concerned himself with that problem.
Their lovemaking had occurred so spontaneously, that
he'd been unprepared to take precautions himself.

Don had been sterile ever since his car accident six
years ago. She wouldn't have been in the habit of
worrying about such things with him.

There were suddenly a million questions that Race
wanted to ask her, but somehow as he stared at the
vulnerable beauty of her very confused face, he just
couldn't frame the sentences. He felt on intimate terms
with her while she did not with him. They were a
million emotional miles apart, and he would have to
give her time to span the distance.

One thing he was sure of: he was taking her to Texas
with him, so they could find a way to work themselves

out of this muddle. He didn't know where he stood with her, and she sure as hell hadn't the slightest idea of where she stood with him.

The passing of time would answer one of his questions. Four weeks to be exact.

During that time he would have to find the right moment to explain everything.

Andrea came to him, her lovely face blushing softly in a mixture of relief and confusion. She reached for his hand, and the light tracing of her fingertips against his skin reminded him of the way she had so eagerly but so lightly touched his body the night before. At the memory a bolt of sexual desire surged through him, but he did not draw his hand from hers. Her nearness was too pleasant, the touch of her making him go hot. "I'm glad you're not mad, Race," she said softly. "You . . . don't know . . . how much I've come to value your friendship. I will always think of you as a very very special friend, who I found when I really needed one the most."

Friendship! He groaned inwardly, and as he stared down into the beautiful innocence of her shining eyes, he wondered if this moment was the ultimate eroticism: a woman who'd surrendered herself to him with the most wanton abandon he'd ever known and yet remembered none of the provocative intimacies they had shared. Now, he knew better than she the brilliant fire of her sensual nature, and she did not know that he knew. Her slightest gestures were charged with sexual memory.

"I also consider you, my dear," he began, forcing a mildness into his tone he was far from feeling, "a very special . . . friend, as well."

Very special. Very special indeed, he thought, smiling.

Suddenly, although he knew he probably shouldn't, he bent his head down to the level of hers and kissed her deeply on the lips. Her mouth quivered at the unexpected onslaught of his kiss.

A shaky tremor helplessly rose up in Andrea, as her body betrayed its secret knowledge of the ecstasy of his. She broke out of his arms, shaking. She was too violently conscious of him as a man.

He saw her fear, and he instantly regretted his action.

"I'm sorry, my dear," he said, "You looked so lovely with the sunlight in your hair that I forgot for a moment that we're just friends."

Chapter 9

DURING THE NEXT HECTIC WEEK, RACE NEVER AGAIN allowed himself to forget that it was friendship Andrea wanted from him. On their way to his ranch, he flew her to Houston first, stopping at the Galleria, one of the world's more elaborate shopping malls, in the midst of a glittering ultra-modern skyline, so she could buy clothes and other paraphernalia necessary to the complicated grooming of a twentieth century woman. Before they left for Hobby Airport, she'd begged him to let her rent ice skates and skate for an hour. He'd watched her as she skated against the background of lavish shops and muted music. He was entranced and amazed by her graceful twists and swirls, her leaps. An audience gathered to watch her, and he realized that she reveled in their attention.

Laughing, her skates slicing the surface of the ice like gleaming knives, she'd skated breathlessly toward him and begged him to join her.

170

"Show-off," he teased.

"I know," she admitted. "I'm shamelessly proud when I'm good at something, and I've always been good at physical things."

He wondered if she knew what her sparkling eyes were saying.

Her smile was provocative. "If I really like a sport I either take a lot of lessons; if that's not possible, I just practice a lot."

He coughed, feeling uncomfortable, unable to stop himself from remembering how good she had felt in his bed.

"Please, Race, skate with me."

"You know Texans can't ice skate," he'd said.

"Maybe you're a natural," she coaxed. "It's like that sometimes with physical things."

Beneath the darkness of his tan, he flushed.

"Come on. For me." Her voice had gone suddenly whispery.

Her invitations were something he apparently couldn't resist. He'd skated then, falling on that slippery, rock-hard, frozen surface more times than he could count, until he'd begun to cling for his life to the glass rail on the edge of the rink.

"Well, I'm not a natural," he'd said as they'd removed their skates afterwards.

Her face had been so exquisitely radiant as she'd looked up at him, her hair a cloud of puffy flame, her eyes sparkling. "No," she'd murmured softly, "but you're a good sport, and that's what really matters. Besides, all you need is practice. You just have to keep trying different physical things until you find an athletic activity you enjoy and want to be good at."

Was she aware of the beguiling sorcery of those slanting green eyes, he wondered, his mind suddenly very far from the subject of ice skating.

She'd reached out to touch him affectionately then,

but he'd moved more quickly than she, picking up their
skates and standing up hurriedly, saying, "I guess I
should return these." He'd been acutely aware of her
outstretched hand, and the sudden look of hurt in her
eyes. But he hadn't dared to touch her. He was
determined to slow the pace of their relationship, and
that was the only way he knew how.

She loved his ranch, and had an instant, deep
reverence for the beauty of his house and paintings.
The moment he brought her inside the natural limestone ranch house tucked beneath live oak and cedar,
on the side of a rocky hill overlooking the placid flow of
the cool, clear Blanco River, and the rolling brown
acres of his ranch, he felt she belonged.

"You designed the house yourself, didn't you,
Race?" she'd asked, as soon as she'd stepped inside.

"How did you know?"

"Because it's you," she'd said simply. The house was
strong and proud and beautiful, quiet and comfortable.
There was no phoniness, no element of disharmony. Its
floor plan had been thoughtfully conceived to achieve
utility, beauty and comfort.

The rooms were large, opening one onto the other.
There wasn't a single hall in the house. Enormous
windows let in the sunlight. Natural woods and stone
brought the freshness of the outdoors inside. She could
imagine glowing fires in the stone fireplaces on wintry
nights when northers blustered down through the canyons and the scrub forests of oak and juniper. The
house was utterly at peace with its environment, as was
the man who lived in it.

"I love it," she said at last, when he'd showed it to
her. The compliment was without design, a spontane-
ous reaction, involuntarily uttered. When she said
those words, she was not conscious of the passionate
allure in her face.

How irresistibly beautiful she was when she looked like that, he thought. It had been all he could do to restrain himself from taking her in his arms, but he made the herculean effort and replied casually, carefully keeping his voice neutral.

"I'm glad you like it. The guest house, where we left your things, is yours, of course. Make yourself at home. We won't start painting until the morning, if that's all right with you."

"Oh . . . it is . . . perfectly," she murmured.

"I have a few things I need to catch up on tonight," he said.

"Of course."

"You must be tired from the trip," he said, slipping into the comfortable stereotype of the gracious host, so he could forget how intensely personal their being alone in his house suddenly seemed. "Would you like something to drink?"

Andrea would not allow him the superficiality of the safe role. Her hands went instantly to her slim hips. She was frowning slightly.

"Race, if I am to stay here three weeks I will not have you waiting on me. That's rule number one. Or acting like I'm a guest."

"I was only trying."

"I know, but don't. Treat me as you would a member of your family." Gently she said, "Think of me as a sister."

He almost groaned in pain. She tilted her face upward and a ray of sunlight shone on her slender throat. Unbidden came the memory of how warmly he'd kissed her there, of the savage pounding of her pulsebeat leaping against his lips. It was only with the greatest effort that he forced his mind to the matter at hand.

"Ah . . . my sister, you say," he replied distractedly.

That was going to be damnably difficult. If she only knew. He tore his gaze from her radiant upturned face, the warmth of her smile having struck him to the soul.

"I fully intend to do my share around here," she said firmly. "I know this isn't a vacation for you."

Their life together fell into the most comfortable routine. It was as if they'd been made to live together.

She posed for him in the mornings when the sunlight flooded his studio in brilliant, golden waves. He wouldn't let her see the portrait he was painting.

She prepared their lunches while he painted. Over lunch they talked of art, of the ruins she'd visited and loved so much, of the ruins she hadn't yet seen, particularly Macchu Picchu—she was dying to go there. They talked of her artistic ambitions, of artist exhibitions and movements they were interested in, of his artistic triumphs. But most importantly, of themselves.

Afternoons, he continued to paint, while she called her stock brokers, studied stock quotations, and read the business magazines she'd gotten behind on. He teased her about her talents in the business world, but she'd sensed his respect and admiration behind his teasing. He was not the kind of man to be threatened by a woman's success, no matter the field.

Sometimes she wandered down to the Indian mound beside the Blanco River. Because of her interest in archeology Race had shown her the mound late one evening, explaining that the Comanches and other tribes had liked to camp where two rivers met. They had favorite campsites they returned to season after season, and after hundreds of years of their waste piling up in one spot, the area assumed the shape of a mound.

Andrea liked to go to the mound because it was a beautiful place nestled beneath ancient Cypress trees that grew like towering green-cloaked giants beside the gurgling Blanco. It was cool, even on the hottest afternoons, in the dense shade beside the river. There she would dig for hours in the rocks for arrowheads, trying to imagine the fierce Indians that had ruled supreme not a hundred years before. She'd acquired a sizable collection of arrowheads in a short time due to her diligent efforts.

"You're like a kid in a sandpile," Race had kidded her one afternoon, when he'd stopped painting early and come down to find her.

Sometimes she saddled Gypsy, a mare Race had said was so gentle a child could ride her, and she rode for hours amidst the sweet-smelling cedar and prickly cactus, loving the freedom of the wide-open ranch with its brilliant panorama of blue skies, with fleecy white clouds afloat in the blue summer haze, surroundings so different from the concrete pavement, tall buildings, dense press of humanity and incessant blare of New York. She felt as though her spirit had been set free.

Race had told her she was not the only city dweller who found the wild beauty of the Texas Hill Country refreshing. Millions of Texans exiled to cities like Houston or Dallas or San Antonio had their roots in the small towns and rough-scrabble ranches and farms of the Hill Country, and they still kept vacation retreats here.

"Condomania," he said with a smile, "has spread even here."

"You make it sound like a disease."

"It is, and a very expensive one."

Andrea loved seeing the white-tailed deer fly before her when she and Gypsy surprised them. There were armadillos rooting among the rocks, jackrabbits scampering behind cactus. Wild turkeys, mockingbirds, and painted buntings as well.

Pure springs fed the rivers and made them clear and fresh beneath the scorching heat of the Texas summer sun, and all too often on the way back from her ride she guided Gypsy along the cool, shaded river, enjoying the solitary sounds of hooves clattering on the stones, of Cypress branches sighing in the breezes. Beneath the shade a few spring wildflowers refused to fade. Golden verbena, fluttermills the children called them, and hardy little rock daisies.

There were caves on the ranch, which Andrea would have liked to explore, but Race was afraid of the caves because of snakes.

"Don't go in them," he'd warned emphatically, having learned she was so impetuous she might do anything just for the sake of adventure, "because I don't want to play hero down there with the rattlesnakes."

"Race," she teased, "I can't get over a big man like you being afraid of anything."

"I'm not afraid of many things," he said a little grumpily. "Just being in the dark with snakes that make nasty sounds when they get mad."

"And sharks," she'd added.

"Hell, Andrea, what fool isn't? Besides, I thought you had an aversion to macho men."

The gentleness in his eyes had wrapped around her heart, and she'd had to look too quickly away.

"I do," she'd murmured a bit shakily, "have an aversion to men like that."

They'd laughed then, and she'd been glad of the chance to hide in their laughter.

It was a glorious time for them both, a time of giving and sharing. The days passed too quickly, and Race found that the right moment to tell her about what had happened on the boat that last night never came. Not that she hadn't asked him. She'd carefully hinted at her loss of memory on several occasions, and he'd sensed the depth of her genuine puzzlement as well as her fear of evoking his anger that she'd misused the drug he'd given her. He was ashamed of the way he played on her fear, and thus prevented a barrage of more specific questions he wasn't ready to answer. He kept waiting for the right moment.

But he was beginning to wonder if he would act even if such a moment should come, because the trust and friendship that was deepening between them was too fragile and too precious to him to risk. She'd been hurt in love relationships in the past and because of this was as nervously skittish as a fresh colt.

He found himself watching her, listening to her intently, searching for any physical change, asking her questions about how she was feeling.

Once when she got hot outside in the late afternoon, and she swayed uncertainly against him complaining of dizziness, he discovered to his amazement a new emotion in the depths of his heart. It was hope. And it triggered other deeper emotions.

He actually *wanted* her to be pregnant with his child. He was in love with her. He wanted to marry her and prolong this week into a lifetime of such weeks. While she . . . As always, he wondered if she cared—just a little. Was she beginning to soften toward him, to think of him, at least sometimes, instead of his brother? He knew she liked the ranch, but was she only enjoying it because it was a vacation to her? Even if she fell in love with him, could she give up New York and her career to live on a remote ranch many months out of the year? Could she be happy here—with him . . . as they were now? Those were questions he didn't dare ask.

Or did she crave the constant excitement she was used to? Hell, she could make her own excitement, he'd laughed more than once to himself.

Time. She needed time, he kept telling himself when he felt almost explosively impatient with the way their relationship was progressing. Then on the seventh day that she'd been with him at his ranch, he was slipping his brushes into turpentine so he could pause for lunch with her, when he glanced outside and saw a beautiful woman's black hair glint in the sunlight as she tossed her head.

Rebecca! A shaft of guilt pierced him. Not once had he called her since his return, and he'd never expected her to simply drive up unannounced. That wasn't her way. He'd been postponing calling her, putting off the moment when he would have to explain his feelings for Andrea. Rebecca was moving quickly up the gravelled drive toward his house, her voluptuous figure encased in jeans and a scarlet blouse that showed off her curves, her face lovely and expectant.

He didn't want to hurt her, but he knew that inevitably he would. At the sight of her, he felt leaden inside, for he understood all too well that his time alone with Andrea had suddenly run out. And it had run out too soon.

The doorbell pinged, its sound like musical droplets tinkling throughout the house, and Andrea instantly dropped the loaf of bread she'd been about to open to make sandwiches on the kitchen counter.

"I'll get it, Race," she called gaily, as she ran lightly toward the front door, wondering who it could be, for they'd had no company in the seven days she'd been there.

The doorbell sprinkled the house with its light sounds again as Andrea threw open the door.

"Hel—" The rest of the salutatory word slid backwards down a throat gone suddenly as dry as the Hill Country dust. Andrea instantly recognized the beautiful woman standing at the door, a woman far lovelier in person than her picture.

"Is Race at home?" Rebecca managed, her voice shaken and filled with doubt.

"He's painting. I'll get him."

"That won't be necessary," came the familiar deeptimbred drawl both women loved. "Rebecca, I should have called you. Come in."

There was genuine friendliness in his voice, and something else that sounded strangely like regret. There was even a certain, distant tenderness in the smile Race bestowed on Rebecca.

Rebecca stared dazedly from Race to Andrea, seeking an explanation, though the explanation was painfully obvious. Nothing was as it had been between them such a short time ago. He didn't come to her and take her in his arms as once he would have. Rebecca knew in that first shattering moment that it was over between them. Yet she was too numb to truly comprehend it, though she'd always known their relationship had never been more to either of them than a means to fill the emptiness in both their lives. She wasn't ready to give him up. Not yet. Not yet.

"Won't you stay for lunch," Race invited casually. He introduced the two women, saying after he did so, "I want you two to get acquainted, to like each other."

All Andrea could do was nod bleakly, thinking his remark one of those utterly inane, masculine things men say sometimes when they don't know what to say. She forgave him instantly, for he couldn't possibly know how miserable she was feeling, how far from wanting *to like* Rebecca she was. And she determined —for him—to try valiantly to pretend she was happy.

"Lunch would be delightful," Rebecca managed, trying just as valiantly, wondering if her own face was as white as Andrea's.

Everything, though the same, was suddenly so different, Andrea thought dismally, once she was alone in the deliberately old-fashioned kitchen preparing lunch. The tavern table, as authentically Texan as the mule-eared chairs that served as the kitchen's rustic furnishings, had lost its charm. Race had told her how Carolyn had scoured antique shops and raided family attics for nearly five years looking for the furnishings of the house, and Andrea had admired his wife's talents and had been enchanted.

The sound of Race's deep laughter mingled with the softer tones of Rebecca and drifted into the kitchen.

Andrea savagely sliced through a slab of turkey breast, cutting ragged pieces. She paused, leaning against the counter as though in pain. In her present mood the splendidly homey room, in which breakfast for twenty could be prepared as easily as tea for two, felt to her as if she were being smothered alive in a prison.

During lunch, Andrea felt increasingly trapped and unhappy. Not that Rebecca and Race meant to leave her out with their conversation of Hill Country people and activities that were familiar to them but not to her, because they did not. It was just that she was incapable of participating in the talk. She felt as tongue-tied as a teenager on her first date, as unenthusiastic as though she were mute, while the two of them chattered with what seemed to her the enthusiasm of two people who held one another very dear and had been parted far too long.

If Race and Rebecca were awkward with each other, Andrea was too upset herself to notice. To her they seemed the perfect couple—both so terribly good-looking. Rebecca so small and feminine, Race so large and masculine as they talked and laughed together. They had so much in common. Their lives had been intertwined practically since Rebecca had been born.

Rebecca began speaking of a barbeque she was having on her ranch the next Saturday. Her beautiful face was aglow with anticipation as she smiled up into Race's smoke-dark eyes.

"Oh, everybody will be there, Race," Rebecca said, "so you must try to come." She turned to Andrea then and said sweetly, though her voice wasn't quite as enthusiastic as it had been when she spoke to Race. "And I want you to come too, Andrea, if you're still here. It will be a typical Hill Country affair, and I think you would enjoy it. At least as a change."

Enjoy it? How could she possibly enjoy a party of Rebecca's, Andrea wondered, when she herself was as hopelessly in love with Race as Rebecca was.

Andrea's mind began a tortured series of thought processes. She loved Race, but what place could there possibly be in his life for a red-headed beanpole like herself; and a crazy beanpole at that, Andrea wondered. But this thought was so awful she didn't dare dwell on it. Instead, she arose at the first possible moment and excused herself, feeling as awkward and gauche as she had at fifteen, like an ugly duckling in the company of two graceful swans. She ran out of the house, stumbling past the ancient stone barn Carolyn had so carefully restored, tearing past the tumble-down rock fence that meandered down to the shaded river.

The sound of her name floated after her in the still, hot Texas air, and she knew Race was calling to her, searching. But she couldn't let him find her—not until she had carefully composed herself.

She hid among the shadows of two enormous bleached rocks that jutted like towering buttresses over the river, where it ran swift and deep and cold. She stared down into the clear water, idly chunking tiny rocks into it, and just as idly watching them ripple the sparkling surface. It was this aimless pursuit that gave her presence away an hour later.

Race's voice came from behind her, so soft and compassionate it was unendurable.

"Are you all right?"

"I'm fine," she muttered, wishing he would go away. She stood up but didn't turn to face him. When he was kind, she felt so defenseless. "I want to be alone, that's all."

"That hint wasn't subtle," he said with a smile, his dark eyes tracing the slenderness of her back with remembered knowledge. He had to restrain himself, to keep from going to her, from touching her.

"It wasn't meant to be."

"Listen, Andrea."

"Go back . . . to Rebecca."

"She's gone."

Surely he must think her actions those of a half-wit. At last Andrea half-turned and guardedly lifted her gaze to the warm black eyes so firmly fixed on her. She flushed at the intensity of his expression. He was so close, so dangerously near, she realized wildly. All week she'd fought against the womanly desires his every kindness, his overpowering virility aroused within her. But now, in her weakened state, she could fight them no longer.

He casually held his hand out to her. "Come on," he coaxed gently. "Why don't we go back to the house?" Andrea moved back a step, retreating like a frightened doe. She was very aware of his coiled strength. He could reach for her and snap her fragile body against his own with frightening ease.

He did not withdraw her hand, and she realized her behavior must seem increasingly ridiculous to him. At last, and very hesitantly she moved forward and placed her slim fingers very lightly into his.

Neither of them was prepared for the shock that touching brought to the other.

It had been seven days since they'd slept together, seven days of his avoiding even the lightest caress, seven days of acute need, and seven days of intimately living together.

"Andrea," he muttered, his low drawl savage suddenly as he drew her into his arms, his eyes blazing with emotion. His hand was at the back of her waist, and he held her tightly against himself, his every male sense vibrantly conscious of her feminine shape molding to the masculine contours of his physique. The way her slender body felt against his—hot and soft—brought back too vividly the memory of the night she'd given herself to him so wantonly, that memory that had lived in his every waking moment despite his ruthless attempt to crush it from his mind; that memory that had tormented him every time he looked at her, every time she smiled at him innocently.

His fingers spread across the small of her back, and her skin felt molten to his touch. Her light womanly fragrance assailed him, and he realized that never had he wanted a woman more. The feel of her, the scent of her intoxicated him so powerfully he couldn't think. All his mental processes were in shreds, his physical needs augmented. Her heart drummed against his chest in wild, abandoned unison with his own.

Her hair was flowing in enchanting disarray about her shoulders and chest, and suddenly the fiery stuff seemed very much in his way. He wanted to touch her, to caress her. He reached up and smoothed her long flaming tresses behind her ear so that the pale, delicate skin of her slender throat was exposed to his touch.

At the lightest brush of his exploring fingers, her pulse jumped, her breath quickening. He smiled at her, captivating her with his tender expression.

"Race . . . what are you doing? Why?"

"Do you really have to ask?" he murmured softly, before he lowered his head very slowly to hers.

Race kissed her then with the pent-up privation of a man who'd gone too long without the sustenance he was most starved for. Her lips were sweet and soft, pliantly responsive beneath his. Exactly as he remembered them; the lines of her body fitted against his muscular frame in the very way he remembered. A strong tremor shuddered through her slight body, and he felt her avid response in the very core of his being.

His eager yearning deepened, and a fierce need for her nearly overwhelmed him. Race covered her full mouth with his kisses. He forced her lips to part and searched her mouth with his warm tongue, holding her small face gently between his strong hands as his mouth explored her with spellbinding intimacy. Then his hands moved lower, stroking her slim neck, caressing the pounding pulse in her throat once more, sliding over her breasts to rub her nipples into stiff, sensitive points beneath the soft fabric of her shirt.

His mouth and his hands were setting every part of her aflame. The fire of shuddering desire flowed like hot waves in her arteries, making her whole body hot and vitally aware of his.

Just for an instant Andrea clung to him as though he were her very life. She savored his masculine passion, the heady feel of him, his complete male arousal. Every sensitive nerve felt rawly alive from his touch, his kisses. Suddenly, this unwanted surge of warmth flooding through her became frightening, and she struggled to free herself.

Never had she felt like this with any man. Never had she known this blistering need, this explosion of erotic urges. And he'd only kissed her. She stared up at him, her face white with shock, her heart beating violently, before she turned away, not trusting herself to look at him.

"No," she murmured, so thoroughly shaken she could scarcely speak. "We mustn't."

"Why not?"

"Because I'm only a convenience. Only a . . ."

"Shut up, Andrea," he said roughly, pulling her back into his arms.

"This is only happening because of Don." Andrea broke off miserably, meaning only that Race had involved himself with her in the first place because he felt responsible for Don. "And there's Rebecca, as well. We aren't being fair to her."

Her words about Rebecca passed over Race's head; he was conscious only of the first reason she'd given.

Don. His brother's name exploded in Race's mind. In that moment, for the first time in his life, he almost hated his own brother because the woman Race wanted for himself loved his brother.

"Can't you forget Don?" he asked furiously.

"What I can't forget is that you and I are not in love. Perhaps by accepting your invitation on your boat and coming here, I've given you the impression that I'm easy."

"Oh, hell. Why do women always say stupid things like that?"

"Because of men and the way they think about us."

"Don't you know me at all, Andrea? You've spent two weeks with *me,* not other men. Hasn't my personality made any impression?"

Oh, yes. Yes. Yes. And that was the problem. *I'm in love with you, you big, handsome dope,* she almost screamed. A blind man could have seen it, but he could not. She stared bleakly up into his searching black eyes, but she had no intention of burdening him with yet another problem—that she'd fallen in love with him. While he was only trying to help her.

"Race," she said very quietly, "I'm going back up to the house and clean up the kitchen."

"Rebecca already did that."

"Oh yes. Rebecca." She choked, swallowing at the sudden tightness in her throat.

Numbly Andrea continued, "I want to forget that this happened between us. It shouldn't have. I don't know why it did."

"Because I'm a damned fool." Race muttered fiercely, his anger raw and savage suddenly. His bronzed hands fell from her slight body, and she felt empty and forlorn as he turned sharply on his heel and strode, in long furious steps, back toward the house and his studio.

He shut himself inside the studio for the remainder of the day, leaving Andrea to her misery alone.

In the brief space of a few hours, everything had gone wrong between them. Rebecca's visit had made it painfully clear to Andrea that Race had commitments elsewhere, while Race was furious with both himself and with Andrea.

He'd known it was too soon to push things between them, but he hadn't been able to stop himself. He'd been aware of the days slipping by, of time running out, of making no progress toward the kind of relationship he desired with her, and he'd lashed out in frustration and pent-up desire. It angered him that she clung to her love for his brother.

He painted with bold quick strokes far into the night, refusing dinner when her pained whisper questioned him through the locked door.

"I'll fix my own dinner, damn you!" he'd hurled irrationally. "When I'm damned good and ready." In that moment he little cared if he hurt her, if the whisper that responded to his outburst was even softer than before.

The next morning, when he came down to breakfast, he was guardedly cool to her, but at least he spoke. He made no apology for his fury of the day before, and Andrea realized that his anger was smoldering just beneath the surface politeness he was determined to show toward her.

A week passed, and the barrier that had risen between them remained. They both hated it though neither realized this, each thinking the other wanted the painful distance, neither trying to bridge the gap out of consideration of the other.

Race threw himself into painting with a vengeance, and he insisted that Andrea paint with him some of the time. At first she felt shy about doing this, her work being so far inferior to his.

That first morning when he'd erected an easel for her, he said, "You keep saying that you really want to paint. Well, if you do, then do it. If you don't, forget it." He thrust several brushes into her shaking fingers. His impatient, black eyes met hers. "So are you going to make a commitment to your art, or are you going to keep saying it's what you really want to do, but never had the courage to try."

"I have tried."

"No. You haven't," he persisted relentlessly.

She drummed the brushes against her hands. She was aware of his steady, intent gaze. "All right," she said at last, accepting his challenge. "I'll paint."

Two days later she'd finished a weird painting of a cat stretched out on a fish platter. An apple with cat's ears hung in the sky where the sun belonged.

Race came up behind her and began to study first the painting and then her own doubting expression, not liking either.

"You don't like it, do you?" he asked.

"No," she admitted. "Not very much."

"Neither do I," he said bluntly in a completely ruthless tone.

She blinked against the tears that threatened to fall. Ever since their quarrel he'd been so uncaring toward her, and her self-control was ragged.

"I always think I will like my work when I start a picture," she began in a quivering voice. "But then when it's finished, I'm disappointed, and I don't want anyone else to see it, especially not you."

"Some of that's normal, of course," Race said in the same cold tone he'd used ever since their disagreement. "Why did you paint this picture?"

"I don't know."

"What do you feel about it?"

"I don't like it."

"Besides that?"

". . . nothing."

"And that, my dear, is at the root of your problem. You need to paint things you care about. Quit trying to be so artsy. Forget every exhibition you've ever been to. Forget what's 'in' in the art world. Forget what the critics like, and for God's sake, forget you ever heard of Salvador Dali and his kind—at least for now."

"But this is my style," she wailed, feeling confused by his cruelty.

"The hell it is. If it was your style, it would ring true. Instead it looks like a copy of something you don't understand at all."

"That's so easy for you to say." she cried. "You're the great George Jordan who can do no wrong. The darling of the art critics. Painting is easy for you. You couldn't possibly understand what it's like for someone like me."

A muscle twitched along the hard line of his jaw, the only indication that he was suddenly as angry as she.

"Quit wallowing in self-pity," he said caustically. "I know it's a pleasant pastime for certain weak-minded personalities, but . . ."

"Weak-minded. I don't enjoy wallowing in self-pity," she snapped heatedly, bristling in her own defense before he interrupted her.

"You do it damn well, love, and with too much enthusiasm for my liking." He paused, considering. "I've thrown more paintings away than you've even dreamed of painting," he continued harshly. "And I put more of myself into them than you've ever put into anything you've done. Easy, you say. It's you who doesn't understand. Not me, or my work . . . or anything else that matters."

"Who are you to speak to me like that?" she cried, realizing suddenly he was speaking of far more than painting.

She turned on her heel and was about to leave the room, but he yanked her back against the wall, upsetting a stack of canvasses that crashed onto the floor.

"I'm not finished with you, not yet!"

"I don't have to listen," she stormed.

"Yes you do," he said. "You're going to listen to every word I say." She struggled in his arms, but he held her easily pinned between his hard body and the wall. "Painting isn't as easy as looking good while a photographer does all the work, is it?" At this comment her scowl deepened ominously, but fortunately she was too furious to speak. "So you want to give up the first time someone tells you maybe you need to think about what you're doing for a change, instead of slapping paint onto a canvas in the style of an artist you admire."

"Ooooo!" She found her voice at last. "You don't mind hitting below the belt, do you?"

"Not if there's a chance of getting through to that stubborn mind of yours."

"Stubborn?" She shot him a killing look.

"Like every other female I've ever known, all you want to hear is my insults. If I didn't give a damn about you or what I think matters to you, I wouldn't say anything. Can't you see that? I'd let you go on painting your unappetizing and meaningless dead cats to your heart's content. I'd . . ."

He kept speaking, his tone harsh, his eyes piercing, his fingers clutching her arms roughly, but all she kept hearing over and over again was, "If I didn't give a damn about you." What did he mean by that, she wondered? Was it only a phrase he'd thoughtlessly hurled out in his anger? Or did he care? Was that why he'd gotten so angry the other day when she made him stop kissing her? Was it because he *did* feel something for her? But if he did, why didn't he say so? They were here together constantly. It wasn't for lack of opportunity.

Two days passed before she found another subject to paint, and when she began again, it was Race himself she chose to paint. With every stroke, she felt that she exposed her heart, her soul, that surely he must see the depth of her love for him.

The days continued to pass too quickly, and she grew so increasingly absorbed in her work, in Race's encouraging remarks and his obvious approval that she scarcely noticed the time sliding so swiftly by. The morning of the barbeque dawned without her having learned the answers to any of the questions she'd asked herself about Race's personal feelings for her.

The phone rang early that morning, and when Andrea sleepily answered it, before it wakened Race in the house, the deep, desperate tones of a man's voice sounded dreadfully familiar.

"Andy, I've come to my senses at last. I love you and only you. I want you back."

"W-what? W-who?" she asked drowsily in confusion.

Her heart began to thud violently. Before the man could identify himself, she had recognized the ardent voice. But she did so with a sinking heart.

It was Don.

As she replaced the phone on the hook, she felt absurdly miserable.

Chapter 10

THE MORNING OF THE BARBEQUE WAS NO DIFFERENT THAN the six mornings that had preceded it. Race treated Andrea with the same distant coolness that was beginning to madden her. The only change was that he did seem a bit more restless than usual; she noted that while he sprawled indolently in one mule-eared chair in a posture that would have grated an antique lover's nerves raw as he read the newspaper, the paper seemed to rustle all the time while he constantly shifted position.

"Is something the matter, Race?" she asked at last, just as incapable of concentrating on her section of the newspaper as he was.

Outside a bee buzzed furiously against the glass above a window box filled with velvety petunias. But inside the kitchen there was a stillness that seemed unnatural, a stillness that magnified the unbearable tension between the two people who couldn't speak to each other.

She had asked him if something was the matter, and her question hung in the air with the bristling challenge of a gauntlet arrogantly slapped at his feet.

"No!" He snapped out the word without bothering to look at her. His antique chair groaned with some movement he made.

"You know if you want me to leave, I'll catch the first plane."

"I don't want you to leave! Why do women need constant reassurance?"

She hated it when he made generalities about women, but she ignored that comment as a deliberate needle to sidetrack her. "Then what is it?" she murmured softly. "I thought we were at least friends."

She heard a low groan from behind the newspaper. It was the man; not his chair.

"Why won't you tell me?" she persisted.

He snapped the pages together and tossed the paper aside, and for the first time all morning his eyes met hers. There was a disturbing intensity in them that she didn't understand before he ripped his gaze away.

"Because I don't feel like it right now, Andrea." Still that smoldering passion that she didn't understand flamed in his black eyes. "If I can't even read the paper in peace, I'm going out. I need some space."

Aching inside, she watched him leave, savoring his size, the utter masculinity of his virile physique. When he was gone, she turned toward the sink to wash the glazed pottery dishes that had been Carolyn's, not feeling happy at all. Carolyn would have understood him, would have understood what this remote politeness meant. Andrea was certain that his mood was somehow her own fault, and it was linked to their quarrel the day Rebecca had dropped by.

Perhaps her presence in his house was making things difficult for him because of Rebecca but he was too gallant to say so. Or maybe he couldn't turn his attention seriously to his work because of her. She would have to try to ask him again.

She wiped the last dish dry, and then she remembered that Don had said he was in Austin and would be driving to the ranch as soon as he could. She'd been so involved with Race and his behavior that she'd completely forgotten to tell him about Don.

Race returned to the house shortly after lunch. "Do you want something to eat?" she asked, when she found him sitting in his studio, brooding in a manner that was very unlike him.

At the sound of her voice he snapped out of his lethargy and moved toward her, the movements of his great body flowing with the grace of a magnificent forest beast.

"No, I don't want any lunch. Thank you, though," he said softly, sarcasm coiling around his politely acidic phrases.

"Then what?"

"What I want—I can't have," he said bitterly.

His attitude was incomprehensibly hostile, and yet there was something else, some other element of passion that she didn't understand.

"Race, I'd do anything to get you out of this mood."

"Would you really, my dear? You're in an unusually accommodating mood this morning, then." His smile mocked her sweetness, and he let his slow, hot gaze travel downward from her gentle face over her slender body until she was blushing.

Suddenly the violence of his long-suppressed emotions swamped him and his arms went round her roughly, his hands moving under the cotton T-shirt she was wearing, against the warm bareness of her skin.

He half expected her to run or to lash out, but she did none of those things. Instead she let her body flow naturally against his.

"No bra, as usual, my pet," he murmured distractedly.

"You know I don't need a bra. That's the only merit I can think of for being flat-chested. I haven't owned one since. . . ."

"You told me," he murmured in soft amusement, his breath a rush of velvet heat against her earlobe. "Since that swimming party in high school when one of the guys at the party found your padded bra folded in your clothes and hoisted it up the gymnasium flagpole with a flag with your name on it. The stupid bastard."

"A low point in my life."

"All young lives have their low points, my darling."

His darling? What was he saying? she wondered, feeling dazed and bewildered and . . . and wonderful.

He was pushing her down into the softness of the wide studio couch and lowering his long body on top of hers. She knew that she should stop him, that she shouldn't let him. But powerful feelings exploding inside her made it difficult to listen to the rational warnings of her mind. After his week of coldness and inexplicable moods, she couldn't resist this sudden unexpected warmth from him, even if it was the wrong kind.

"This is crazy, Race. We've scarcely talked for a week," she managed in a whispery tone that was so filled with desire it did little to stop him.

"Crazy is the right word, Andrea," he said, gently nuzzling her slender throat with his warm mouth until shafts of quivering sensation pulsated through her. "I'm crazy for you. Crazy about you. Crazy because of you."

He kissed the feathery edge of an amber brow. She moved her head, and his mouth found her lips.

It was a slow, hot kiss, tantalizing her past the point of no return. It was a kiss that drugged her senses, lulling her doubts. The long fusion of their lips allowed Andrea to enjoy the slow arousal of her own desire.

"You're what I've been needing and wanting," he admitted, his breath falling against the sensitive flesh at the hollow of her throat.

"I want you, too," she said, "more than I can say."

His hands roamed lazily over her slim body, molding her to his hard length.

"I suppose it's just physical," she murmured.

"Maybe it's more my sport . . . than ice skating," he teased as his lips nibbled against her soft skin.

"Maybe . . ." she smiled.

"And yours, too," he added, knowing full well that it was.

"We'll see . . ." she whispered seductively.

"Mmmm." His face was buried in her hair. "You smell so sweet. Is it perfume?"

"No." His mouth moving along the cord of her neck was making her feel deliciously hot. "I don't wear perfume . . . usually."

"Then it is simply you," he said, caressing her. His lips became warmer and more passionate, his body harder and more urgent, his hands seeking, exploring, loving.

She shouldn't let him. But Andrea hadn't the strength to resist when he pressed his mouth once more to hers. She lay powerless beneath him, accepting the hard possession of his lips, the gentle intimacies of his caressing fingers, the mastery of his embraces.

His hands burned over her pale skin, removing her garments one by one as though he were unveiling a precious and much-beloved art object. His lips followed the path of his hands, kissing each newly exposed part of her until it was dewy moist and achingly hot from the torrid rain of his kisses.

She shouldn't let him do these wildly primitive things to her, these intensely private things. He made love to her as no one had ever made love to her, and she was unprepared for the splendor of sensations his tender assault evoked. She shouldn't. Oh . . . but it felt like she should. . . .

"Don't," she murmured half-heartedly, feeling wretched at the thought of him stopping.

"Forgive me . . . if I can't," he said, expelling a swift sigh of defeat. "It's more difficult to stop every time I hold you and kiss you."

It was more difficult for her, as well, especially when his lips traced such tingling paths across her naked flushed skin, when his hands made her feel so lush and voluptuous, so womanly.

"How much longer will you be able to stop . . . yourself, little one? It's not just me that wants this," he whispered knowingly as his mouth touched the bright tendrils that were tangled from his kisses against her pale face.

He kissed her then, more deeply than ever before, wondering if she would freeze in his arms or surrender to the needs of her body.

Everything he did aroused her soft flesh to the hard demands of his. Her body trembled, her breath fell unevenly. She was quivering like a frightened lamb. She choked back a helpless sob as all her will to resist him fled her, and the pagan needs of the flesh reigned joyously supreme. Her small hands stole slowly around his broad back, and she drew him down to her.

A glorious feeling of exalted triumph flooded Race at the exact moment of her capitulation, and he crushed her to himself with fierce male joy.

Flames of desire consumed them, their wild, abandoned passion soldering them together in a series of long breathless kisses. She was clinging to him, crying for him, begging him.

Breathing heavily, feeling sure of her now, he stood up to hastily undress himself. At the separation of his flesh from hers a cool draft fanned her perspiring skin, and she shivered in the air-conditioning. She watched him, reveling in his hard masculine beauty, noting the powerful corded muscles of his thighs, the hard curved line of his hips, his narrow bronzed torso, his muscled chest. He was the most magnificent of men—as handsome as the boldest lust-filled pirate prince, and she loved him.

He looked at her. Never had his eyes been darker as they swept her, loving her, desiring her. Her own heart was thudding violently. There was a sudden tightness in her throat, a leaping exhilaration that raced through every nerve end in her body.

"Race, we should be careful."

At first he didn't understand.

"I mean," she said, "I could get pregnant."

His dark face was very still, his expression intense with some emotion she didn't understand as he regarded her.

"Don't worry, love," he said at last. "I'll take the necessary precautions."

He left the room then, and when he returned, he knelt beside her and took her hand in his, rubbing her fingers and the tops of her knuckles. For a long moment he stared at her, losing himself in the soft liquid eyes that beheld him. He was scarcely conscious of what he did as he leaned over to brush his lips gently across the soft fullness of her pale rose-hued lips, and dreamily she closed her eyes momentarily as fierce tremblings of desire shuddered through her body. His kiss became more urgent, his mouth roving, plundering hers before his head moved lower to caress and suckle the sensitive nipples that arched to fill his mouth invitingly.

Her whole body seemed to tingle. There was an odd feeling in the pit of her belly that his every kiss intensified. It was like a fire burning low before an explosion.

She was moaning faintly, sighing in surrender, shuddering at his touch, at the delicious waves of sensations his male body roused in her.

He was so hot-blooded, so all-male—everything she could want in a lover . . . in the man she loved. Strangely, as he took bolder and bolder liberties, she felt no shyness. It was as if this wasn't the first time between them, as if her body was perfectly tuned to the desires of his, as though she knew what he was going to do before he did it. She opened herself to his mouth that had moved still lower between her parted thighs to fondle and plunder and slide with delicate softness against the very core of her femininity. Everything blurred in a sensual haze as he stroked her and kissed her. She was conscious only of the slow, deliciously languid eroticism of his lovemaking. He knew how to rouse her until feverish passionate needs thundered through her, and she called out to him, begging that he take her completely.

He sat up, and for a long moment his eyes lingered on the drowsy passionate beauty of her glowing face. He was looking at her still as he slid inside her, filling her with a strange hot pressure, that built and built and built until a shocking burst of incredible pleasure shook her. It was as though a million stars exploded, as though an unutterable volcanic heat engulfed her, as wild rippling pleasure tore through her in cascading hot waves.

And when it was over—it lasted still—the fusion of mind and heart and soul, the sharing closeness she felt toward him.

He was hot and she was hot, and the air in the room felt cool against their moist, over-heated bodies. They were wrapped in the bold, warm color of his paintings which blurred, like images of a collage.

She ran her hand through the damp softness of his raven hair, a feeling of dazzling love for him washing over her.

They lay together a long time, their bodies still intimately joined. They fell asleep in satiated contentment despite the shower of sunshine spilling over their bodies in a veil of brightness.

When she woke up some time later, she saw that he was already awake, though he was lying very still and silent so as not to awaken her.

"I want to kiss you now," she said very softly.

He smiled at her, his dark eyes alight with wanton memory.

"Do you know what I mean?" she asked, feeling shyness for the first time.

Inexplicably, he chuckled. "I know *exactly* what you mean," he said, his male face suddenly eagerly enthusiastic in anticipation as she wrested her small body from his.

"Perhaps . . . I should shower first," he ventured.

"You don't need to."

"Then we'll shower together later . . . afterward," he smiled, remembering a certain wanton memory of their first shower together that always gave him great pleasure.

"Sometimes I think you must be a mind-reader," she said, wondering at his intuitive understanding of her.

"Mmmmm." He was too content to feel even a qualm of guilt, and he was no longer thinking of her words. His entire nervous system was tuned only to her delicate manipulations of his hard male flesh.

A gentle breeze gusted through the limestone hills, carrying with it the sweet perfume of cedar, the swishes of cool air softening the intensity of the late-afternoon heat.

On the terrace to the back of the house beneath the

dense shade of the live-oak trees, Andrea and Race sat together in two widely spaced rocking chairs sipping mint-garnished iced tea from tall frosted glasses. The runners of their chairs squeaked softly as they rocked back and forth.

Andrea wanted to speak to him, but she couldn't. Neither could Race speak to her. They were each too wrapped in wonder at what had happened between them. Yet they shared an intense closeness despite their inability to communicate with words.

Into this intimate haven of loving togetherness walked the one man who could rend it asunder with his mere presence.

Don's carefully polished shoes fell heavily on the rough gravel drive as he walked purposely around the back of the house, carefully picking his way, having rung the front bell to no avail. Even though he'd loosened his tie because of the heat and carried his jacket slung over his back, he was perspiring so heavily his dress shirt clung to his damp body.

"I thought I might find you two back here," Don called cheerily when he caught sight of them, mopping his wet brow with the back of his hand.

The blood drained from Race's dark face, while Andrea's pale skin flushed to her hairline at this forgotten and yet expected intrusion.

Race rose slowly to his full height. "Don. What are you doing here?" he asked in a voice that sounded strangely dead.

"Didn't Andrea tell you I was coming by this afternoon?"

"No." The single word sounded as dark as Race's now glowering expression. He swerved to stare meaningfully at Andrea. "Why didn't you mention it to me?"

What could she say? "I . . . simply forgot . . . to tell you," she stammered at last.

"That iced tea sure looks good," Don remarked casually, completely unaware of the undercurrents between his older brother and Andrea.

"I'll pour you a glass," Andrea said, glad suddenly to escape both Don and Race who seemed suddenly so furious at her again. She hated the way he could so easily fall into a black mood. She blamed herself, of course; she should have remembered to tell him about Don's coming. "Do you take sugar?" she asked mechanically.

"One teaspoon, please. Don't you remember?"

She spun quickly away, shaking with a strange sensation of uneasiness at Don's obvious attempt to remind her of the intimacy of their former relationship.

When she returned, Don was chattering amicably to his stony-faced brother. "On the way over I stopped by Rebecca's. She told me all about the barbeque tonight." Andrea handed Don his glass of tea, and he addressed her as she picked up her own. "Andy, don't you think Rebecca's a stunner—just the right kind of woman for Race? She's exactly like Carolyn. Like all the women he's been involved with."

Andrea went white, and she set her own glass of tea back down before she dropped it.

"Don, I'd really prefer that you change the subject from Carolyn and Rebecca," Race stated coldly. "I don't like my personal life discussed like the latest chapter in some novel you're reading."

"Sorry, old boy. Didn't mean to rub you the wrong way."

"Didn't you?" Race looked angry.

"Damned touchy today, aren't you?" Don asked, not taking the hint.

"How I am today or any other day is none of your concern." Race snapped.

"You're right, of course," Don said easily.

"Where's Linda?"

"That's why I came by this afternoon. You see, she's left me."

Race exploded. "I can't believe that."

"Yes. Well, she has. She had a whole list of reasons—a mile long she said. I didn't ask her to catalogue them."

"She would take you back if you went after her."

"Perhaps. But the point is, I'm not going after her. Our marriage has never been what a marriage should be. I've come to my senses on that score. Andy's the woman I want, not Linda. I want to thank you, Race, for seeing after her when I couldn't. I'm afraid I haven't behaved too nobly to either Linda or Andy. But, I'm going to change. Now that I no longer have to live a lie."

Race strode angrily toward the house. "I'll leave you two to talk then. It's obvious you have a lot to say to each other."

"Race." Andrea called after him, his attitude stabbing her with pain. But the slamming of the screen door in her face was his only answer to her summons.

"Frankly, I'm glad he went inside," Don said. "He's in a bastard of a mood, and I didn't help matters with my news. He's always championed Linda's cause."

"It's my fault he's in a bad mood, I'm afraid," Andrea said dismally.

"Don't go blaming yourself for Race being impossible."

"He's not impossible." Andrea defended. "He's nice."

"Of course, he can be nice at times. But he's cursed with an artistic temperament that won't quit. He was born with it. I should know," Don said vehemently. "I used to blame myself for it, 'til I finally learned that's just how he is. Plus, he thinks that he can run my life just because he's my older brother."

"Perhaps I should go inside after him."

"Leave him be. He needs to be alone when he's like this. I can't stay married to a woman because he thinks I should." Don said. "Besides I didn't drive out here to try to figure my brother out. That's as pointless as trying to figure out why the sun is shining or a dark cloud is hovering. I came here because I'm flying to New York tomorrow and I thought I'd take you with me. I wanted to see you, to tell you. . . ."

The eagerness in his voice terrified her.

"Don't." she said, backing away from him.

"Andy . . . I know you're mad because I lied. But I can explain all that on the plane to New York."

"Mad?" She wasn't mad. She'd been hurt and broken-hearted. Terribly disillusioned. But so much had happened since that night when she'd discovered Don was married. It was almost as if she'd become a different person and was living a different life. None of that mattered any more. She no longer cared whether he was married or not, because she no longer cared about him in the same way.

"But don't you see I *had* to lie?"

She looked at Don's passionate, spoiled face beneath his stunning thatch of golden hair. What she saw was that to him it had seemed the expedient thing to do at the time, and he was the kind of person who took whatever the easiest course toward a goal was. Why hadn't she seen the kind of man he was before?

Because, a tiny voice in the back of her mind replied, she hadn't wanted to. Don had been a dream that she had wanted to believe in because she had needed to. She'd been afraid of being alone. She'd been raised to believe that a woman needed a man to believe in, and Don had simply been there. Of course, the irony was he had never been there for her. She had been there for him—to fill in the gaps in his life that his marriage had left empty. A sort of dessert on a side tray to be sampled when the main course wasn't enough.

"I knew," he continued, "that if I told you the truth you would never have given me the time of day."

"How right you were. And now that I do know . . . "

"But don't you see, honey, I won't ever have to lie to you again?"

"It's too late now, Don," Andrea began, attempting to explain at least a part of what she was feeling. "I don't want any kind of relationship with you. Whether you're lying or not. Everything you told me, everything I thought about you and believed about you was interwoven with the one central lie you told me. I don't even know you, and quite honestly, I'm not sure I want to."

She was as stunned by her speech as he was, amazed that she could speak so coldly to a man she'd thought she'd loved not two weeks ago.

"But, Andy, you can't feel that way. Not when I've given up Linda, and by doing so put my political career on the line, given up everything that means anything to me because I love you."

"Damn you." She choked back a sudden feeling of rage. She knew he was twisting things to his advantage. Putting her in the wrong instead of himself. "Don't try to lay a guilt trip like that on me. Go back to your wife. I'm sure if I let you give up all that for me, eventually you'd decide I too wasn't worth it." Suddenly, as she was reminded of the happier times they'd shared, her face gentled; once, his presence had filled a few gaps in her own lonely life. "Take care of yourself, Don," she said very softly, "and . . . I . . . hope you can find the way back to your marriage. I really do. You have two very beautiful children. There's too much divorce these days. Please, think about trying again . . . for their sakes. Because even if you leave Linda, no relationship will ever be perfect."

She would have left him then, standing there on the

terrace open-mouthed, his tanned face pale with shock at her rejection, except he caught her hand in his in a last-ditch attempt to force her into changing her mind. He pulled her hard against himself.

She knew he was going to kiss her, even before his lips began their descent, and she stood very still waiting for him to get it over with.

When his mouth met hers, she felt nothing other than a certain coolly detached curiosity, and as he drew away, for the first time that afternoon he knew that she meant what she said.

"But what are you going to do?" he asked at last, in a low, defeated tone. "I could still take you back to New York with me. I know you don't intend to stay on with Race forever. While it was great of him to help you through that rough spot for me, I know that basically you two can't possibly really be enjoying one another."

"No . . ." she murmured, remembering Race's moodiness and periods of distant politeness.

"I guess you're in the guest house, and he's given you the run of the place."

"Yes . . . I've done a lot of riding and painting." She was feeling uneasy suddenly at his probing her so very precious relationship with Race.

"Tell me. Have you driven him to the limits of his patience again? He was so furious about you in Cancun after that bus trip. I can't believe you've spent all this time together without his having a few more black tantrums. You're not his type at all, you know. He's used to such docile, passive women—except for Carolyn, that is. But he was into that before he knew what hit him. All he saw at first was how damn good-looking she was. Race has always been so narrow-minded in his tastes in women."

"Really?"

"You've seen Rebecca, I know."

"Yes."

"So you know the type he likes. She's like Carolyn, in looks anyway. The resemblance is amazing. Rebecca's sweeter, though."

"Is she?" Andrea mumbled, for want of anything more coherent to say.

Would he never leave? She didn't want to hear about Race and how ill-suited they were to one another. But Don apparently had nowhere else to go, and he stayed for what seemed an hour, skipping from subject to subject without noting she wasn't interested in any of them.

It was only when Race's truck roared into the front drive that Don remembered the time.

"Guess Race is mighty anxious to see Rebecca the way he's gunning that motor of his. Haven't heard him do that since we were kids."

"Rebecca . . ." Andrea murmured forlornly.

"Yes. His truck is heading straight for her ranch."

Andrea stared at the beige swirl of dust billowing behind the truck like a great parachute behind a jet.

Race was leaving—going to Rebecca, when there were so many things she wanted to tell him.

Suddenly Andrea wondered if they had anything at all to say to one another, and she knew she couldn't bear to stay and find out that they hadn't.

She would leave with Don and go back to her New York and the crazy gaudy world where she belonged.

If Race wanted her, he would come after her.

And if he didn't. . . .

Chapter 11

THE TRUCK JOUNCED OVER THE ROUGH COUNTRY ROAD past a sparse population of placid Hereford cattle grazing on long dry grass. The road wound through rough cedar-choked canyons the river had carved deeply into the terrain. Race, who was driving much too fast, scarcely noted the enchantment of the countryside scorched with the blazing colors of a blood-red sun.

He was angry—at himself, at Don, and at Andrea. Most of all he was angry at himself, since he was the biggest fool of the three. He should never have allowed himself to hope that he could change Andrea's heart when he'd known all along she loved his brother. But she'd seemed so soft toward him at times, and this afternoon. He pushed the painful memory aside; it drove him crazier than anything else.

The terrible vision of Andrea wrapped in his brother's arms, his brother's mouth lingering on those same soft lips he himself had possessed with such utter completeness only hours before, assailed him. Race had come to the kitchen, intending to tell her that it was time for the barbeque, when he'd seen them from the window.

For the thousandth time Race asked himself what kind of woman was she that she could give herself like that to two men on the same day?

Not my kind of woman, he thought furiously. And yet . . . in so many ways she was. And as always some part of him gave her the benefit of the doubt.

Perhaps there was still a chance for them. Maybe all she needed was more time. Damn it. He felt acute frustration. He didn't need time to know that he was in love with her.

No matter what happened, he'd decided to go to the barbeque to talk to Rebecca. Even though he hadn't the vaguest idea where his relationship with Andrea was going, he had to set Rebecca free. She'd been too wonderful to him through the years, for him to use her by hanging onto their relationship when he knew that he was in love with someone else, even if he couldn't have the one woman he knew he wanted.

In spite of everything, he wanted Andrea. Wanted her past sanity. Past . . .?

His thoughts were abruptly cut short as he topped a hill at too high a speed, and saw too late that a plump black Angus cow had ambled into the middle of the road. The cow stared vacantly at the truck in those last seconds before Race swerved, and the truck began skidding on loose gravel. There was nowhere to go but over the side of the rocky hill.

The truck rolled, and Race was thrown free, his body hitting the hard limestone ground with a violent impact, before he too rolled, following the path flattened by the truck.

There was an explosion that shattered the quiet of the countryside, and intense heat as a great orange ball of fire consumed the truck and sent black waves of smoke billowing against the red sky. Rocks were tumbling over disturbed grasses. Excited wildlife fluttered and ran to find new cover.

There was pain in his chest everywhere, pain more intense than anything Race had ever felt before. He tried to move, but couldn't. Then trauma and shock obliterated all sensations save for a terrible feeling of coldness. The coldness too was finally snuffed out, and a soft, peaceful blackness covered all.

Race's battered body lay ten feet down the hill, out of sight of the road and the motorists who might chance by.

Overhead a solitary hawk soared in search of its prey, a single moving creature in the vast desolation of scrub brush, cactus, rock hills, and rough oak trees.

Andrea was breathless from carrying her suitcases up the flight of stairs to her quaint apartment on Waverly Place in Greenwich Village. It had once been a carriage house for a Victorian mansion that had long ago met its fate with the wrecking ball. The key jangled in the lock, and wearily she pushed open the door of her apartment.

A vague musty scent assailed her nostrils. The rooms had been closed too long. Her green eyes ran over the familiar furnishings before she stepped inside, seeing and yet not seeing the beige couches, the bold surrealistic paintings on the white walls, walls that were so ancient they were webbed like precious porcelain with tiny cracks, the faded Oriental throw rugs, the stacks of investment periodicals, the archeological knick-knacks she'd collected in her travels. It was a mad, scrambled hodge-podge that she loved.

Lightning sizzled against a window; thunder rumbled, shaking the window panes. She could hear the rain rushing down the gutters to the street below. It was a depressing sound, accentuating her feelings of loneliness.

She was aware of a vague lingering scent of tobacco smoke. She saw that a cigarette had been carefully crushed in the center of a crystal ashtray. Who . . . ? She stood frozen, staring at the ashtray, her heart pumping wildly as her imagination pondered one terrible possibility after the other.

Suddenly her loneliness was forgotten. She didn't want to go inside. She wanted to run screaming back down that darkened staircase into the downpour outside. She knew, without knowing how she knew, that someone had come into her apartment while she was gone. Someone, an alien spirit, had moved about *her* things. He had smoked, and carelessly . . . or not so carelessly . . . deliberately, rather, so she would know he had been there. To terrify her.

Fear made her skin prickle to the back of her neck. All the terror that she'd left behind was back. She felt as though someone had just socked her in the pit of the stomach and left her gasping. Waves of nausea, worse now than during the turbulence on the plane, engulfed her, and she sagged weakly against the door frame, clutching it for support. Fiercely she fought back the silent scream that crawled up her throat.

She tried to tell herself she was being ridiculous. There was no reason for her to think someone had been in her apartment. This was just an attack of nerves. Perhaps a friend had come by that last day she'd been in New York, and she didn't remember it.

No. She would have emptied the ashtray when she'd carried the garbage out. She knew her habits too well to trick herself like that.

Despite her fear she forced herself to step inside and close the door. She shot the bolt home and leaned against the door for a long time. She would have to learn to live with fear, she supposed, if she was going to be such a ninny. This was her home, where she belonged, and she wouldn't allow herself to be driven away again.

She dully noticed other things that were different, her magazines had been flipped through and tossed back onto the table by someone unfamiliar with her system for organizing them; the window shades were no longer pulled down as she had left them.

Unbidden came the thought of Race. She yearned for him, knowing that if he were here she would feel safe instead of terrified. As Don had driven her from the ranch to Austin, her heart had cried out with every mile they traveled through the rough country hills, every mile that separated her from him. But she'd told herself that if she meant anything at all to him, he would pick up the phone and call her. How fast she would go running back to him. She'd almost hoped, almost believed she'd be greeted by a ringing phone.

Moving mechanically about the room at last, she picked up the silent phone and lifted it to her ear to assure herself there was a dial tone, and then she set it once more into its cradle.

Just as soon as she set it down, she lifted it nervously once again, hesitating before she dialed. She needed to call Luci to let her know she was back in town and ready to go to work.

With quick, agitated motions, her long, slender fingers dialed the memorized number of Luci's elegant townhouse just off Park Avenue.

"So you're back," Luci said briskly as soon as the necessary amenities had been disposed of. "I can't tell you how glad I am of that."

"I'm glad, too," Andrea said weakly.

"You don't sound like it. Are you sick?"

"Just a little upset stomach."

"Something you picked up in Mexico?"

"I don't think so."

"Well, see a doctor, just in case." Luci sounded genuinely concerned. "I once had a friend who went down there and picked up the most horrible liver fluke."

Luci, a bit of a hypochondriac, was always full of such stories, and Andrea listened dutifully, glad that the subject had been diverted from herself for the moment.

"The most horrible thing happened while you were gone," Luci began, plunging into another story with her usual relish.

"Mmmm," Andrea replied absently. She was having difficulty digesting the liver fluke story. "What?"

"Then you haven't heard what happened to Kim?"

Something in Luci's voice snapped Andrea to attention. "No."

"Well, my dear, it's the wildest story you ever heard. I still hardly believe it. There's this man, this psycho or something who has hassled a few models lately. I didn't know a thing about it till this happened, but it seems it's been going on for months. One of those sugar daddies who hangs out at the bistros and restaurants popular with young models—you know those awful men that are always cruising around the model agencies in their gleaming Mercedes-Benzes and Cadillacs offering the girls free rides to their next bookings—"

"Yes?"

"Do you know that a waiter at Yellowfingers Restaurant told me the other day he has offers all the time from those men of more than a hundred dollars just for a model's phone number?"

"I tried to warn Kim about all that, Luci, but she's not too smart when it comes to men."

"Well, I don't think this was her fault, poor dear. One of those guys just went berserk. I mean crazy-crazy! He called a few girls and said weird things to them late at night. Very unpleasant little man. A couple of girls were nearly raped in their buildings."

Andrea collapsed into the chair beside the phone, the strength draining from her legs. She felt shaky and cold and numb as she stared fixedly at the squashed cigarette butt she should have thrown out the minute she walked in the place.

"What happened to Kim?" she managed at last, a sudden, dry fear in her soft voice.

"The guy ran her down with his car!"

"What?"

"Fortunately she saw him at the last minute and jumped down into a concrete stairwell leading to a subway. His car crashed into the building, and the police have him in custody. Kim broke her leg and fractured her wrist, but other than that, she's fine. She's in Mount Sinai Hospital."

"I'll have to go see her," Andrea said mechanically.

"She would like that, poor dear."

Despite Kim's tragedy, Andrea felt vaguely relieved, for she could not stop herself from relating what had happened to her friend to her own frightening time.

When the terrifying phone calls that had plagued her before her trip to Mexico did not resume, she began to believe that perhaps the danger was past, that the man the police were holding was indeed the man who had been calling her. With every day that passed, her fear lessened. She had no more nervous attacks, and slowly she began to lower her guard.

A week later, Enrico dropped by and asked Andrea for dinner. Andrea had just gotten in from an exhausting day, a double booking. She'd spent the morning posing for the cover of a fashion magazine, and the afternoon taping a cosmetic commercial.

She'd washed her hair and showered and was wearing only a loose bathrobe. Her damp hair was bound tightly in a lavender turban. She let Enrico in as soon as he identified himself, reluctantly taking the dozen long-stemmed roses wrapped in crinkly green tissue he thrust into her arms.

"You really shouldn't have, Enrico. I know you couldn't possibly afford these."

"Don't remind me of the acute state of my finances," he said, waving his arms in a theatrically extravagant manner that once she'd adored and now found affected. "I came over here to forget about all that. I was in the mood for Italian food and I thought of *Angelina's*, and then I thought of you."

"You can't afford that either. Did you ever think of an Italian TV dinner?"

He grimaced. "Never."

Angelina's had been their favorite place to eat when they'd been married, and Enrico still invited her there with great regularity. She knew he did so to remind her of their former intimate relationship.

She sighed in exasperation. If only she hadn't answered the door. "Enrico, I really am very tired. I've had five back-breaking days of work."

"After three weeks of vacation," he finished. "Come, doll, a live wire like you can handle dinner with a friend."

She wondered how he knew exactly how long she'd been gone, but then he had a gossipy streak and knew lots of things about everyone in the business.

"I'm not feeling like much of a live wire these days," she murmured.

"What's wrong? You sick?"

"No. . . . It's nothing I can really put my finger on. I just don't feel like myself."

"That's all the more reason for you to have dinner with me. It'll make you feel better."

"It amazes me that you want to go out with me—

your ex-wife—when you always have a string of dazzling, much-younger protégées to choose from."

"Because I do not think of you as an ex-wife," he said, suddenly so serious that just for an instant, before he smiled, she felt alarm.

"Enrico, I wish you would accept our divorce."

He swept about the room in his theatrical manner, as if he still lived with her. "Never."

"You say that as emphatically as you rejected my idea of a t.v. dinner," she said with a giggle; he really did look pompous and ridiculous strutting about in his grand way.

He threw back his head and laughed. "That is why I married you," he said at last. "Because you always make me laugh."

She stared at him, suddenly serious herself. "I've always wondered why you did marry me, Enrico."

"Because I loved you, of course." he snapped impatiently.

"Love . . ." Her voice trailed off as she studied him intently for a long moment. He'd never been faithful to her, even in the beginning of their marriage, though it had taken her two years to discover this. Love was a word people wrapped around all sorts of less noble emotions. He had not married her for love, of that she felt sure. She was too tired, however, to pursue the thought, just as she was too tired to argue with Enrico when he was determined about something.

"Okay," she said mildly. "I'll go out with you . . . if we go Dutch."

"No argument there," he said with a smile. "That's another thing I can't afford—a big check."

The Italian dinner with Enrico had some compensations. At least when she didn't stay in her own apartment alone at night, she could concentrate on something other than her silent telephone and Race. Still, there was such a disturbing intensity about Enrico that she suddenly found herself regretting having dinner with him in the softly glowing candlelit dining room where once they'd come when they'd been in love. He kept reminding her of nostalgic memories she only wanted to bury. She felt curiously on edge.

Enrico was full of news about the latest developments on the *model-maniac,* as the man who'd tried to run down Kim was called in the newspapers. Enrico seemed to have an avid interest in the subject. He had worked with some of the models over the last few months. They had been terrified by the man.

Enrico did most of the talking, and when he did not, long awkward silences fell between them. Several times she almost confided in him about the telephone calls she herself had had and about the Buick that had almost run her down. But some instinct kept her from telling him.

When he finally asked her about Don, she confided that she no longer cared for him. Enrico had known all about Don, for once in an attempt to try to make Enrico understand that she would never go back to him, she'd angrily told him about Don. However, she did not tell him tonight about her love for Race. Enrico seemed to relax after that, and because he did, she did, too. Toward the end of the evening she almost found herself enjoying herself.

But when she had shut the door on Enrico and his protestations that she let him stay the night, and she was once more alone in her apartment, an incredible depression, more hopelessly intense than ever before, settled on her.

The phone rang several times, and always when she answered it, there was a breathless catch in her voice, an agonizing fluttering of butterflies in her stomach while she waited in that split-second of suspense before the caller identified himself, and always when it wasn't the voice of the man she loved there was the terrible sensation of aching loss and disappointment.

Race didn't call—not that evening or any evening in the weeks that passed.

She was madly, painfully, hopelessly in love as she had never been in love before. It was ridiculous that she should be feeling what most women felt at a much younger age. She'd scarcely known him any time, but it felt to her as if she'd known him for all time.

With him she'd felt she was the woman she'd always wanted to be.

Her upset stomach lingered, and she began to wonder about it. She would feel queasy at the oddest times on buses, in elevators, or in passing a fast food restaurant where the air was thick with the smell of grease. She was strangely more aware of odors—of cloying perfumes, of diesel exhaust. Subways were the worst of all, the way they jerked and threw her about, and she gave up riding them altogether.

One bright sunny Sunday afternoon Luci had invited her to lunch at Tavern on the Green, in Central Park.

They were sitting amongst the elaborate crystal and flower decor beside a window that looked out onto the deeply shaded park. White-coated waiters rushed with swift efficiency from table to table. There was the tinkle of laughter and the blur of voices engaged in pleasant, leisurely conversation.

"I do like to come here on Sundays," Luci was saying, "because it's always so busy with tourists and so on."

Andrea nodded sympathetically. She understood the older woman's loneliness too well. One could lose oneself in a crowd, and sometimes one could almost forget.

When lunch arrived, Andrea found to her dismay that she had no appetite. She merely toyed with her food, hoping that Luci who was chattering quite energetically about her health would not notice. However, during a lull in the conversation, while Luci searched for a new topic, Luci's sharp eyes noted a plump broiled shrimp sliding from Andrea's fork back onto her plate. Andrea set the fork down.

Luci pushed her glasses firmly up the bridge of her nose and studied Andrea closely for a long moment, seeing her well for the first time.

"You don't look at all well, Andy," she said. "Frankly, my dear, I'm beginning to worry about you. I never see you eat a bite any more, yet you're putting on weight."

"I couldn't be."

"You look a little puffy, like you're retaining water. Leave off the salt at once. When we're through here I want you to go home and crawl in bed. Did you ever see the doctor about that stomach virus?"

"No."

"Well, do so at once. Remember that horrible liver fluke."

"Please . . . don't remind me of that," Andrea begged, the last shred of her appetite irrevocably ruined by the memory of that tale.

"Promise me then?"

"All right . . . just so you'll stop worrying."

"Pregnant?" Andrea stared at Dr. Maddreys' plump, gray face, feeling utterly dazed. "There . . . there must be some mistake," she gasped.

"I can assure you, Miss Ford, there is no mistake. I had the lab run the test twice. Both times it was positive. By my calculation the date of conception was . . ." He pulled out a pencil and tapped a square on his calendar with utter certainty. "Along about here."

Because of the glare on the glossy page of the calendar, Andrea had to lean forward and strain to see.

The bold black number mocked her, and for a moment she felt a strange sense of unreality.

That . . . that was when she'd been on Race's boat. Three weeks before the last day she'd spent on his ranch. She went as white as the medical drape she was wearing.

"Miss Ford, are you all right?"

She sank back onto the table, feeling faint and shaken. Race had made love to her on the boat, and he hadn't told her.

What kind of man kept such a thing to himself?

Suddenly she was remembering the strangeness of his actions that last morning on the boat, his awkwardness with her, his intuitive knowledge of her that she hadn't understood. He'd known things about her that she hadn't known he'd known. He'd tried to keep a distance between them at first, until the last week. Had he thought her easy? Was that why he'd been so determined to seduce her again? At this point it was painfully obvious that he hadn't really cared for her.

At first she felt wild fury and betrayal. Then as her first powerful emotions abated, a low, burning anger that was so intense that it felt close to hatred began. When she remembered the six weeks her phone hadn't rung, she felt even more sharply hurt than ever before.

She was carrying his child. He must have known all along there was that possibility, and he hadn't called.

Dr. Maddreys' voice was gentle. "Is there any possibility of the man marrying you?"

"I don't think so . . ."

"I'm sorry," he said. "You know, of course, there are options. Adoption."

"Dr. Maddreys," she said emphatically. "I will be thirty-three years old when this baby is born. I'm running out of time to be a mother. I want this baby—even if I wouldn't have planned things this way. I want this baby more than anything I've ever wanted. I have enough money so I can stay home for a while—until I feel like going back to work. You see," she said, "I have no one else."

When Enrico called that night, she told him about the baby. She was so wrapped up in her own feelings that as she chattered on and on about her plans for the baby and about a certain gorgeous brass baby bed she'd seen in a window on Madison Avenue, she didn't notice his strange silence. At last when she finally paused, he spoke.

"Who's the father?"

"I . . . I didn't want . . . I don't want to tell anyone about him—not even you, Enrico. He was just someone I met in Mexico . . . and stupidly fell in love with. A mistake. It didn't work out. That's all."

Enrico, who knew her well, heard the gentle sob at the end of her brave speech.

"Stefano said something." Enrico hushed himself at once.

"What about Stefano?"

"Nothing. I've forgotten, really, what I was going to say. Well, I wish you the best." His voice was cold.

She realized suddenly that she shouldn't have told him, for despite his own modern lifestyle, he retained his old-country values and did not approve of alternate lifestyles such as divorce or unwed mothers. Not that she wanted to be an unwed mother; she did not. It was an unpleasant fact that was forcing itself upon her.

Another week passed and she found herself thinking more and more of the baby, even as her feelings toward its father hardened.

One Saturday afternoon, soft gray rain was pouring gently onto the sidewalks and pavement as Andrea walked home from the grocery store, keeping away from the curb so as not to be splashed by passing vehicles. The light had burned out again in the stairway of her building, and she kept her eyes downcast as she mounted the stairs, for she was very careful these days when she climbed them. Thus she didn't see the powerfully built giant of a man in his London Fog hunched in the shadow beside her door.

"Andrea?"

The deep, beloved-hated voice vibrated through her with shuddering intensity.

"Race!" For just an instant her heart stopped.

"What are you doing here?" she demanded shrilly, her soft voice reaching a squeaky note that wasn't her own.

"I want to see you," he said very gently. "I have to see you."

"Well, I don't want to see you!" Liar, her heart cried out. Just seeing him now, briefly in the hall, knowing he didn't care, was almost more painful than she could endure. "Go away." she cried. "Do you have any idea what you're doing to me?"

"Please, Andrea, I'm begging you."

Something in his voice, some trace of sincere humility caught at her heart. She was still so vulnerable to him—so much in love with him, and she despised herself for her lingering weakness toward him.

Blindly she began jabbing the keys into the key hole. Quiet tears that she hated began to fall, and she was shaking so violently she could scarcely stand.

He hesitated a moment before touching her, but he could not stop himself.

Bronzed fingers closed over her trembling fingers, and he turned the keys in the lock.

She hadn't looked at him until that moment, but his touch . . . his nearness . . . were doing odd things to her. His warm fingers lingered on hers. She glanced up, and saw him well for the first time.

In the gray light, his handsome face seemed paler, thinner. His black eyes were darkly shadowed as though with pain. The grooves beside his mouth ran deeper, and she wondered at the cause. He didn't look well.

"I didn't think you would ever come," she breathed at last, admitting, though she didn't want to, how much she'd wanted him to.

Time stood motionless as he caught and held her gaze. "I had to come, you little fool. Did you think . . .?"

"You never called."

"Neither did you, and you left me, remember? Besides, I was afraid to call."

"Afraid?"

"There are some things that are difficult to say on the phone."

"You could have come before now," she said.

She turned from him then, and walked into her apartment, knowing that she would die inside forever if he did not follow her.

"No, Andrea, I couldn't, and that's why I was afraid to call." He was looking at her, and his black eyes were so intense and loving that she began to hope wildly. A tremor ran through her that left her feeling weak and dizzy and terribly strange before her legs crumbled, and she sank down onto her soft beige couch.

"This is a crazy place," he said tenderly, his eyes taking in the wild, bizarre paintings and the zany knick knacks littering every table. "Just as crazy and lovable as you are."

For the first time she noticed that his movements were not as graceful as she remembered, his strides slower and stiffer. He was so white. So thin.

Suddenly the last remnant of anger and hurt pride fled in her concern for him.

"Race, what's wrong? You're . . . limping."

"I was trying not to."

"What?"

"My truck turned over."

She got up, and took his hand gently in hers, drawing him toward the couch. "Can you sit down?"

"Very slowly."

"When did it happen—the accident?"

"The day you left."

He told her of the long night on the hillside, when he'd been only half-conscious, of Rebecca's brother finding him the next morning, of his three-week stay in the hospital, of his slow convalescence on the ranch.

"As bad as it all sounds, the doctors keep telling me how lucky I was to be alive. But when the pain was so bad, I found that a little difficult to swallow."

"Oh, Race, and I thought. . . ."

"What did you think, love?"

"That all this time you didn't call because of Rebecca. Because you didn't want me."

"Rebecca will always be a dear friend, but she's not the woman I love."

"Oh."

"She and I had a long talk one day before I came home from the hospital. I think she already knew how I felt even before I began to explain."

Andrea scarcely dared breathe. A wild fluttering hope winged through her.

"It was only when Don came to see me in the hospital two weeks after the wreck that I found out you had not gone back to him. In fact, he told me a lot of things that surprised me."

"Like what?"

"Like you and he . . . you had never slept together."

"Did you think we did?"

"I'm afraid I tormented myself with that particular misconception," he admitted.

"Well, I'm glad he talked to you then," she murmured.

"So am I." He paused. "He and Linda are seeing a marriage counselor. And I want to thank you . . . for talking him into trying again. Linda really is the most wonderful woman, and if Don could ever commit himself to her I think he might see that."

"I'm so glad Don decided to do that."

"Andrea, I came only because I had to see you again. You left . . . before we ever had a chance to talk. There were certain things I needed to tell you."

"What things, Race?"

"Oh . . . certain things that happened," he replied vaguely. "Feelings."

His words fell into a deepening pool of silence, for he could not go on. Perhaps later, he thought, when he felt more comfortable with her.

"I see," she murmured, feeling disappointment that there must still be barriers between them. She almost blurted out her news; she was fairly bursting to. The sentences were already formed and trembling on the tip of her tongue. But she sensed his hesitation toward her. Somehow she summoned the will to remain silent on the subject for the present, because she knew if she did not do so, she would be pushing him into a relationship he would feel compelled to accept. She did not want to bind him to her with knowledge of the baby. Not now. Not ever.

"I've moved my things into my co-op on Park Avenue," he said. "I like New York this time of the year. When the air is cool and the leaves have turned." Again he was staring at her with an intensity that left her breathless. She was aware of his mouth, hovering inches from hers. He reached toward her and spun a wayward tendril of flame around his finger. "When the leaves have turned . . . the exact shade of your hair," he finished softly, before his face lowered to hers, and his mouth closed over her shaking lips.

The crush of his mouth ignited a slow-sweet fire in her arteries. For an instant his grip tightened upon her shoulders before he deliberately gentled his touch.

Andrea curved her arms around his neck, and fingered the thickness of his black hair. The drizzle outside had left his hair damp and silky. The male scent of him enveloped her. She was scarcely aware of anything beyond the dizzying wonder of his kiss.

"Oh, Andrea, it's been such hell without you."

With masterful ease he unfastened buttons and slid soft fabric aside. His hands moved over her, caressing each soft, white part of her. His large hands cupped her breasts, and vaguely she wondered if he would notice that they were larger than before, that her body was different.

A low moan escaped Andrea's lips as tremulous waves of sensuality washed over and over her, until she felt wet and wild and wanton as though they lay with their bodies fused on a deserted windswept beach with a violent surf crashing warmly over them.

It was too soon for the answers to certain unspoken questions between them, but it was not too soon for love. And it swept them away on its wildly glorious tide.

The windows of Andrea's apartment suddenly went dark. Outside a man stood in the shadows of the building opposite Andrea's and watched as the shades blackened before he jammed his fists deeply into his coat pockets and strode angrily on his way.

Chapter 12

DAZZLING SUNLIGHT SPLASHED INTO RACE'S OPULENT
co-op, bathing the lovers in their bower of love. The
enormous bedroom was serene and modern in decor.
The lofty, soaring shape of all seven rooms were
spanned with enormous windows, satisfying the artist's
need for an abundance of light.

Andrea lay in the great bed, her gaze drifting over
the appealing furnishings. Floors and beams were red
oak bleached to a pale cream; walls and sloped ceilings
were covered with raffia in almost the same shade.
Stuffed chairs were upholstered in white canvas, and
the bedspread that Andrea had neatly folded was made
of the same crisp fabric. Andrea particularly admired
the gleaming dark wood of two antiques, a round
Georges IV table and a Regency commode, because
they made stunning accents in the light room, as did the
shiny black polished cotton on two Louis XVI arm-

chairs. On every wall hung fabulous paintings, some of them Race's own work, but most of them part of the collection Race had spent a lifetime carefully acquiring.

Deeply contented, Andrea snuggled against Race. Twenty floors beneath them the streets were abustle with scurrying pedestrians and streams of bright yellow taxis, but the two inside the lavish penthouse were nestled in their own private cocoon.

"You said you were painting my portrait. You never said you were going to paint me nude," Andrea said in playful petulance, sitting up in Race's great round bed to study the enormous canvas of herself that hung on the far wall. She gave her head a little shake, and red waves of hair splashed over her pale shoulders and slender back. She was as naked as her portrait.

"I never know for sure what I'm going to paint until I paint," Race evaded smoothly, studying the woman in his arms and not the painting.

"It's flattering," she said with a smile, the female in her liking that aspect of the painting. "I'm much skinnier than that!"

"You're not a pound skinnier than that! In fact, you're not nearly as skinny as you were." The shape of his brown hand molded itself around the gentle rise of her belly.

"Are you going to exhibit it?" she asked quickly, moving away from the warmth of his hand, not wanting him to pursue that thought. As she looked at the picture of herself she was flushing. She felt a strange sensation of modesty, for there was such an intimate quality about the picture. It undressed more than her body.

"What kind of question is that?" he asked, no longer amused. "Of course not. It's much too personal to exhibit. I painted you for myself. An artist must do that from time to time. There are simply some subjects I must paint whether they are commercial or not. Not that I couldn't demand a king's ransom for that work, which I could. There is great demand for erotic art."

Erotic art. There was a faint tremor of excitement in her voice. "Surely you don't consider *me.*"

"You're very erotic." His hand traced a tingling path down the length of her spine and when she shivered, as a hot glow began to spread throughout her body, he smiled knowingly. "And I captured your erotic spirit on that canvas, little one. There is something in your smile . . . a promise, a secret . . . the hint of bold-nesses. Every time I look upon it I go hot with the memory of you, just as I feel hot now . . . with you in bed with me."

His voice had changed; his smile had deepened as he regarded her. A warmth flowed through her, and she felt her senses slowly awakening. The mood of friendli-ness was gone and in its place was the beginning of passion.

Race lowered his head to nibble the tips of her breasts as he began to stroke her belly and thighs.

Andrea moaned, forgetting the painting and every-thing else, even the glorious succession of days and nights they had had together since Race had come to New York.

Every nerve thrilled and quivered to his caressing touches.

Violent tremors quaked through Andrea's warm body as Race's mouth touched each swollen nipple and his long fingers roamed over her body, exploring her intimately. Reality receded in a sexual mist that left her achingly aware only of the darkly muscled body of this man she loved. All she knew was the touch of his stroking fingers, his hot caresses, his burning kisses. Reveling in his lovemaking, she instinctively reached toward his bronzed, lean body poised over hers, and encircled her arms about the muscular breadth of his wide shoulders, drawing him closer, so she could press her feverish, soft flesh to his.

Race lowered himself, careful to move slowly because of his mending ribs, settling his weight against the wanton swaying of her hips to complete the act of love, to lose himself in the sweet, seductive warmth of her.

A storm whirled around them, the storm of sexual desire and love, and they were consumed by it.

Much later they sat together beneath a bright yellow and blue canvas awning and trees on Race's terrace and looked down upon the lush greenery of the park. Race withdrew his hand, wrapped tightly around Andrea's, and lifted a silver fork. Andrea, in a mood of total tranquility, was absorbed with the view. The scurrying people beneath seemed so small and far away—unreal. It seemed to her that she and Race were the only two people in the world.

Race sliced into a fluffy piece of angel food cake. "For a skinny girl, you're a very good cook."

"I don't know which to react to—the compliment or the insult."

"Why don't you surprise me, and go for the compliment?"

She met his white smile with a pert one of her own. "I can't go wrong on that kind of cake with you."

"Nevertheless, it's very good. Do you realize this is my third piece today. If I don't slow down, you'll be in the kitchen cooking another one, and I'll be as fat as that teak Buddha butterball on the mantle."

"I'll cook you all the cakes you can eat."

"How many does this make since I've been in New York?"

"Three."

They both laughed.

Andrea leaned over the railing to peer down at the people streaming past on the sidewalk.

"I love it up here, Race. And I feel so happy and safe."

He looked at her oddly. " 'Safe?' Strange word."

"Not really." She let her eyes meet his, deciding at last to tell him. "I left New York and went to Cancun in the first place because I was so terrified here." He was the first person she'd ever confessed this to. It was evidence of the growing trust between them.

She told him then of the phone calls and the car that had nearly run her down. She told him too what had happened to Kim.

"Why didn't you tell me this before?" he asked her, his face dark.

"I didn't tell anyone. I thought it was something I could handle on my own."

"Naturally."

"But, Race, even though I keep telling myself that the man has been caught and I shouldn't be afraid. Sometimes I still am. There's something very insidious about someone deliberately wanting to hurt you. There's something irrational about fear."

"I suppose it takes a while for something like that to wear off."

"It's just that on the phone the man sounded as if he hated me so much. And I know this is going to sound crazy. Sometimes I still feel that voice hating me, and I think of that man out there hating me. Feelings that intense don't go away, do they?"

"Sometimes they do," he said gently, "given enough time." He took her hands in his, to communicate some of his strength to her. "Andrea, I'm glad you told me, and now I don't want you to worry about it any more. As you said, the man's been caught, and I'm here in New York now. The danger is past."

What he said was true, yet strangely, her vague sense of uneasiness remained, even in this moment of supreme shared happiness with Race. She knew that when she suddenly found herself alone on a deserted street or subway, she would be afraid. Whenever the phone would ring late at night, she would feel a twinge of her old fear.

Deliberately she brushed these thoughts aside and forced herself to smile brightly. "What would you like to do this afternoon?" she asked softly.

"I don't have the strength . . . for what I'd like to do," he replied huskily. "I guess that leaves us no options other than work."

"Slave driver," she teased.

Race and Andrea painted together later that afternoon as they'd done so many of the afternoons since Race had come to Manhattan. Race's studio had skylights sliced into the soaring, sloping ceilings, as well as banks of windows across two walls.

"I like what you're doing better now," Race said from behind her shoulder.

She jumped.

"I didn't mean to startle you."

"It's still not like what you do," she murmured, basking in his praise, as his arms gently slid around her tiny waist. She liked the feel of his hard male shape against herself. "But I sort of like it myself."

"No . . . it's not like mine, but it shouldn't be. We're very different—you and I. Even though your subject is treated in a very original manner, what you're saying will touch a lot of people." He let his callused palm stroke her slender back; he loved touching her, being with her.

"And that's what I want to do," she exclaimed. "I want to paint incredible things and make them so believable that people will feel the world I'm painting is real. I want to draw them into my paintings. The things I want them to believe in don't really exist as tangibles in our world, you see."

"At least now, you know why you're painting what

you're painting. You've come a long way in a very short time, Andrea."

Race studied Andrea's painting. The head of an intelligent but bored-looking girl of a bygone age was swathed in a hat that looked more like a silk fish than a hat. There was something very modern about her expression that captured the viewer's curiosity and drew him into the picture. On the girl's dainty gloved hand perched an orange rooster. Three strange monsters napped beneath a tree filled with golden pears. More nonsensical creatures roamed in a dark woods. Suitcases were piled high beside a whimsical boat.

"The girl is traveling, don't you see," Andrea said with quiet pride, her green eyes softly aglow as she looked at Race. "She's someone I sketched in an airport on my last trip to Rome. People always look so bored when they travel, and yet there is something so exciting about traveling. I wanted to say something about boredom and the lure of the exotic."

"Is that why you travel, little one?" he asked tenderly. "The beckoning lure of lost worlds?"

"Something like that," she admitted.

"I think I'm beginning to understand you a little. Ancient places are like your paintings, not quite real. And yet once they were so very real. Far enough removed from reality so you can feel safe."

"You're not making any more sense than I do, but you're awfully close," she said, laughing. "Do you know where I've been dying to go for simply ages?"

"Tell me."

"Machu Picchu. In Peru."

"You told me in Texas."

Her eyes were sparkling, and as he lifted her paintbrushes from her hands, his own eyes matched hers in brilliance.

"I'm tired of painting," he said. His brown fingers

moved lightly at the back of her neck to untangle a flame curl that had caught itself in the neckline of her T-shirt.

"Lazy," she teased.

She was very aware of the movements of his hands against the sensitive cord of her neck. A shockwave tingled down her spine.

"You wouldn't say that . . . if you knew what I had in mind," he whispered huskily, his breath warm against her cheek.

"I take it back." Her voice was strangely breathless as he drew her even more closely against his hard body.

His smile deepened, as he felt her instant leaping response, her passions now as thoroughly aroused as his. He liked her fire as well as her softness.

His feelings were so intense they overcame him.

"Andrea. Oh, Andrea. . . . My darling."

He lifted her heavy hair in both of his hands and smoothed it away from the delicate oval of her pale face. Then he lifted her unresisting arms around his own neck so that the front of their bodies provocatively touched. He felt powerful and swollen against her, on fire for her as her body melted to the heat of his.

He buried his fingers in the silky masses of her hair and brought her face to his. Very gently he kissed the warm parted lips.

His hands slid down her slender back, folding her soft, thinly clad body to his hard masculine frame. She fitted him so exactly, so perfectly, that he groaned with the flaming sensation of awesome feelings that surged through him. He felt an intense building pressure, an acute need that he could not stay.

His mouth traced a path down Andrea's satiny-smooth throat, as his expert hands began to undress her, unbuttoning, unfastening, slipping soft fabric from her pliant body. Her clothes fell unheeded to the polished red oak floor, pooling in soft splashes of vivid color beside her slender ankles.

Race's hand shaped the gentle curve of each breast, lifting the soft swells of flesh for his lips to taste their taut sweet fruit. His dark head was bent low over her as he suckled both pink peaks until they hardened against his lips.

Andrea felt breathless and lightheaded. He lifted her high in his arms and carried her toward his sunlit bedroom. He was a giant of a man, and he carried her as if she weighed no more than a feather. It was an exhilarating feeling to be swept away; Andrea loved nothing more than feeling small and feminine.

"I like it when you carry me," she said in a tiny, soft voice.

"Do you?" he mused, smiling down at her. "I suppose you acquired the taste for it when I picked you up at that diplomatic affair in Mexico and hauled you up those stairs in front of everybody."

"I did not! I was horrified."

"Come on. You weren't thrilled . . . even a little bit?"

"No."

"Hmmmm. I was. That was a first for me. What did you call me that night . . . a barbarian, a pirate?" He chuckled. "I rather liked that."

"You would."

"You have to admit that was a hell of a compliment— for a man who's never considered himself very macho, because he's got a healthy fear of things like snakes and sharks. And that was one hell of a kiss. After-wards . . ." he said, remembering. "Maybe you like it when a man treats you rough?"

"That isn't what I like at all," she said coyly as he pulled back the crisp white covers and laid her upon his bed.

"Then show me what you like," he said, amusement at her show of temper mixing with his passion.

"All right."

She drew his hand down to her body, drawing his fingers to secret, womanly places. She loved it when he touched her as though he longed to discover everything about her. The mattress dipped with his weight as he lowered himself beside her.

Andrea caught her breath and then rolled on top of him, melting against his body as her fluid warmth covered him.

"Careful," he whispered with a groan.

"I keep forgetting about your ribs," she said guiltily.

He liked her lightness as well as her angelic sweetness and concern for him.

"Sit up a bit, and I'll be fine."

She readjusted her body over his, and he ran his hands over the smoothness of her. He was staring up at her, his black eyes ablaze with passion.

"I want you to love me, Race," she murmured quietly.

She brought her face down to his. Race's lips closed over hers, and he did not speak. His tongue licked the soft fullness of her lips tantalizingly, and then thrust into the silken depths of her trembling mouth.

Andrea's fingers wound into his thick, wavy, black hair and caressed him. He moved deeply, settling her firmly against himself, his muscled body dancing with hers in wild, mind-splintering splendor. They moved together with the fierce soul-binding exhilaration of lovers made for each other.

Burning shivers shuddered one after the other through her, and her fingers tightened convulsively about his muscular shoulders. She clung with a terrible consuming love for him.

Together they soared on the wings of love to ecstasy.

A lavender haze enveloped the gray silhouettes of stacked buildings jutting in the distance across the verdant expanse of the park. Sam Sanderson, Race's most prestigious art dealer in the city, as well as an old and dear friend, had invited Race for drinks at the Plaza and then dinner afterward. Andrea had declined the invitation, having told Race she preferred to work out a few of the problems she'd encountered in her latest painting.

However, after the tumultuous lovemaking in the afternoon, she felt too lethargic, now that Race had gone, to pursue any mentally energetic endeavor. Instead, she'd bathed and dressed, did some light housekeeping that couldn't wait for the maid on Monday, and made another angel food cake, now baking in the oven. The delicious flavor filled Race's co-op with the most marvelous aroma.

Having accomplished these tasks, she wandered back out onto the terrace to admire the view. The setting sun was deep gold and flashed in window panes like bars of light. Its soft slanting rays tinted the buildings rosy hues and showered deep shafts of light through the branches of the trees to light up brilliant patches of lawn. Even cities could be beautiful, the artist in her decided.

The view hypnotized her, and she marveled that she'd spent so much of her life in New York on the second floor of a tiny apartment when she could have had a view such as this one. Of course, she'd wanted to save her money for investments. She'd known that despite her enormous income and her momentary fame, she couldn't really afford to fritter away her money on an extravagant lifestyle. She'd needed to use her money wisely, so that when her face and body no longer commanded top fees, she could manage without her salary.

She thought of the days she and Race had spent together, of her ever-deepening love for him, of his tenderness and passion toward her. They had not addressed certain important issues between them; they had simply spent their time being together. She had not told him of the baby, though she wanted to more with the passing of every day.

As she thought of the baby, she longed for a son . . . black haired and tall like Race, she wished dreamily. Suddenly she wanted very much to be with Race, and she wished that she had not forced him to go out without her.

The telephone buzzed, and thinking it was Race, she ran lightly through the living room to grab the princess phone on the kitchen counter.

"Hello?" Her voice was sexily husky.

"Hi, doll. I haven't heard you sound like that in years," Enrico snapped with a brittle chuckle.

"Enrico." she said, her sexy tone instantly evaporating in a whiff of disappointment. "How did you find me here?"

"It wasn't easy."

"Are you all right? Do you need something?" she asked guiltily, for her booker at the agency had told her about Enrico's repeated calls. She'd simply been too involved with Race this past week to return them.

"I need to talk to you—now. I'm downstairs."

"Downstairs?" How had he? "Couldn't we make it some other time?" she asked aloud. For some reason she didn't feel right about having Enrico at Race's place.

"I've been calling all week. It's an emergency."

There was an element of urgency in Enrico's low tone that alarmed her.

"Are you in some kind of trouble?"

"I need to see you, now."

Still she hesitated.

"Please?"

His voice was strangely deep, and she shivered with a chill.

She couldn't remember Enrico ever saying 'please' before. "All right," she agreed at last, not wanting to humiliate him, for he was a man with old-country pride.

She regretted her decision the instant Enrico slammed the great varnished oak door and burst into Race's co-op. He seemed on the verge of exploding with nervous energy as he moved rapidly about. His eyes blazed with fierce passion as they explored everything with a passionate intensity. Andrea hadn't seen him like this since the day she'd told him she was divorcing him.

"This is a hell of a pad," he said bitterly, as his dark eyes took in the fabulous collection of carefully selected art and antiques, all displayed in a pleasing manner of careless elegance. Carolyn's expert touch. "I can see that now that you've decided the days of your very successful modeling career are numbered, you've decided to move up in the world by grabbing the first rich man that happened by. George Jordan. Famous, to boot. Who would have thought?" He turned the full power of his dark, malicious eyes on her. "I can't help admiring your uncanny ability to succeed, Andrea. Whatever you touch turns to gold. You never make mistakes, do you? Ah yes. Our marriage. . . . I suppose you considered that a mistake, one you had to hastily tidy up the way some people sweep dust beneath a sofa. The minute something doesn't work out in your life, you simply discard it and move onto something else that looks more promising. I should have said before that you don't waste time worrying about your mistakes; not that you don't make them. You're too keen on whatever new project you're into to worry about the past. You won't even return my calls . . . now that you're set on catching bigger prey."

Andrea had grown as violently angry as he the moment he'd begun his attack. A hot pulsebeat hammered against her throat. Her green eyes raged. She rushed to the door he'd just entered and threw it open. She stood beside it, her slim body quivering.

"You can leave, Enrico, if that's all you came to say," she said in a voice dangerously soft. "And keep your nasty remarks to yourself. I've bent over backwards time and time again to help you with your debts. What haven't I done for you? How many ex-wives?"

Enrico moved toward the door—not to leave but to slam it shut once more. He turned the lock with a swift, ominous gesture, that made her feel trapped.

"There's the rub, Andrea. . . ."

His voice had changed subtly. It had deepened, and it was so terrifyingly familiar she wanted to cringe at the sound of it, though for the moment she couldn't remember where she'd heard it before.

"Is that cake I smell? It is. You never used to cook for me, and now you're cooking for him."

"So what, Enrico?"

"So what, you say. So everything."

Her heart was still pounding, but with a different emotion, that left her breathless and chilled as she weakly clutched a nearby chair for support.

His terrible, dark, glowing eyes were fixed on her, hating her, as he strode menacingly toward her. She released the chair and backed slowly away from him, out onto the terrace.

"Enrico, what is it?" She felt afraid—and so cold, though the night air was unusually balmy. She was shaking as a chill shuddered through her slender body.

It was the same feeling that the midnight telephone voice had engendered.

Suddenly she knew.

Enrico was the man who had called her, who had haunted her, who had tried to run her down. Enrico was the man who hated her. And suddenly when she remembered his violent rages during their marriage, his craziness, his possessiveness, she knew she had good reason to be afraid.

"I've never considered you an ex-wife, Andrea," he said gently, and his voice was suddenly even more terrifying, his dark eyes more piercing.

If only he would stop looking at her like that. It made her remember the things about him that had made her dread his touch.

But he kept staring at her fiercely. "When I saw you that first day beneath the Statue of Liberty, I knew I had to have you. You were a star. You were going places. I wanted to grab you and go along for the ride. You didn't know what potential you had, but I saw it instantly. I didn't make you into a star. You were born one. You had a face that fascinates on film. You make love to a camera when you smile, when you move. And those eyes. No one in all the world has eyes like you, Andrea. They say things that can drive a man crazy. You have the sultry eyes of an enchantress in the face of an innocent. Anyone could have seen what you were. But I found you first. You belonged to me."

"People don't ever belong to other people, Enrico," she said, attempting to reason with him.

"Wives belong to husbands," he said coldly. "I need someone like you, can't you see?"

"Enrico, it's over. It's been over for years."

"That's what you say. But I don't agree. You belong to me."

"No, Enrico, I don't."

"Then if I can't have you, no one can."

He reached for her slender throat, and his hands closed roughly over her shoulders, his fingers digging into her flesh. She felt the rough stone wall grinding into the small of her back as he pushed her hard against it.

He was so strong. She felt like she was fainting as his hard hands pressed her skin bruisingly against bone. But she mustn't, she couldn't faint. There was the baby . . . and Racè,

"Enrico . . . you're hurting me. Stop."

"I never wanted to hurt you," he said, almost tenderly. "Beauty like yours is a sacred thing to me. I wanted you because I knew I would never have to worry about money with you around to make it and worry about it for me."

"You make as much as I, Enrico. You're famous in your own right, and your skills are more enduring than mine. It's just that you spend too much. If you'd use the smallest amount of judgment. . . ."

"If I had your disciplined personality," he snarled. His hot breath fell heavily, unpleasantly against her face. "But I don't. I needed you. I owe people now . . . who'll kill me if I don't pay them. I have nothing to lose."

"I'll help you," she pleaded. "Haven't I always helped you in the past?"

His hands were cruel vises twisting the delicate skin around her neck, pressing down against her windpipe, snuffing out her ability to breathe. He held her cruelly, no longer caring that he hurt her.

"The other models told me about the man calling them and following them in his car, and I thought that maybe if I scared you like they were being scared, you'd be afraid alone and come back to me. But no. Not you.

I should have known that any plan would backfire with you. You went off to Mexico and found another man."

His fingers were tightening on her throat, and the edge of brick bordering the top of the stone wall cut into her back. The only response she could make was a low, desperate gurgle.

A loud insistent alarm began to blare, and when his fingers slackened on her throat, she jammed a fist against his hard chest and wrenched free. She sank against the far wall of the terrace and panted. He was too near the door for her to risk trying to run for it. For the moment it was enough just to be free of the torment of his crushing fingers.

"What is that?" Enrico growled, as the shrill, nerve-shattering sound continued.

"I think the cake's burning," Andrea managed faintly. "I'll . . ." She made a move toward the glass door. "No."

The telephone buzzed again and again.

"Enrico, it's the smoke alarm. All I have to do. . . ."

"I can't think what to do with the phone and that blasting noise." He sagged against the wrought iron table.

Seizing his weakness as her opportunity, Andrea bolted toward the sliding glass door in a desperate attempt to escape, but Enrico sprang quickly out of his momentary lethargy and moved more swiftly than she, jumping in front of her in a single bound. He snapped her to him with the playful viciousness of a cat who grabs a mouse he's been tormenting and only set aside for a moment.

"Not so fast, doll," he said with a malevolent leer. "I haven't finished with you yet."

He dragged her to the furthest corner of the terrace and bent her fragile body back against the low wall again, holding her this time so that her head dangled over the edge upside down. She could see the pavement in a terrifying spiral twenty stories beneath her. All Enrico had to do was slide his hands beneath her body and heave her over the edge.

Her heart plummeted from her stomach toward the pavement, and it lodged like a painfully throbbing live thing in her parched throat.

"Race . . ." she murmured faintly. "Race. Please come . . . help me."

Chapter 13

"Till death do us part," Enrico muttered savagely over the blare of the smoke alarm and the telephone that had begun to jangle again. He pushed Andrea's body another inch over the ledge. "That's the vow we took, wasn't it? Don't worry, Andy. I'll be right behind you. I can't make it without you. I never could. That's the whole problem."

"Enrico, for God's sake," she screamed. "I'm pregnant. You don't want to hurt an innocent baby do you?"

The blood was rushing to her head, and seemed to pound through her brain. The hands gripping her body hesitated. Enrico had always had a fondness for children.

"Let her go!" boomed a terrible voice from behind Enrico. Andrea knew it was Race's. "If you hurt her, I'll . . ."

When Enrico didn't instantly oblige, he was yanked

bodily from Andrea and thrown hard against the wall of the building opposite her. He slid down the bricks, drooping like a broken puppet.

Gently Andrea felt herself sinking into strong arms. Race folded her tenderly to him, his warm hands stroking through her hair as though she were a small child he sought to comfort. Slowly, gently he placed her on a low bench, making sure before he left her that she was all right.

Then he turned back to Enrico just as Sam Sanderson and two bellmen strode onto the terrace.

Enrico was pulling himself to his feet just as Race reached him. Enrico lunged desperately toward Race, trying to hit at him with both of his wadded hands.

"You bastard," Race growled fiercely, as he jammed his fist into Enrico's face, shattering his jaw. Blood spurted from Enrico's nose over Race's hand as Race hit him a second time, and sent him sprawling.

"I wasn't going to hurt her. Not really," Enrico muttered, cringing like a cowed dog with angry eyes as Race walked toward him. "I just wanted to scare her, to make her see that she belongs with me."

"The hell she belongs with you. You twisted, sadistic creep."

Sam Sanderson laid a restraining hand on Race's shoulder. "He's had enough, Race. There's no more fight in him."

Race's great chest was heaving. He stood looking down at Enrico in disgust. He decided that Sam was right, and that Enrico wouldn't be giving them any further trouble, at least for now. Race combed his hand wearily through his thick black hair that had tumbled across his brow. He wiped the back of his arm across his face, staining it with a mixture of sweat and blood.

"You need help, Enrico," Andrea said shakily. "More help than I can give you."

"Get him out of here." Race growled savagely, going

to her while Sam and the two bellmen quickly grabbed Enrico and hurried him out into the hall.

Race knelt beside Andrea, and his dark expression gentled slightly. His face was white from pain, and she knew what his efforts must have cost him, since his ribs had not yet healed from his accident.

"Race . . . you're hurt," she said softly, stroking the bloody place above his eyebrow.

"I'm all right," he said roughly. "But are you?"

Tears of relief began to spill over her amber lashes, down her pale cheeks as she tried to nod bravely. Suddenly she was shaking as he drew her into his comforting arms. Now that she was really safe, all the terror and hysteria that she'd locked inside herself for months spilled out of her. She began to cry, and she didn't know if she'd ever stop. She felt like such a cowardly little fool.

Only vaguely was she aware of his soothing voice, of his lips in her hair, of his fingers lightly dabbing her damp cheeks with his handkerchief. She felt shattered inside.

She cried and cried until at last she could cry no more.

Much later—after the police had come and gone, after Race had fixed her a martini and insisted that she drink it, she began to feel more herself again.

Race and she lay in bed talking.

"Why did you come back?" Andrea asked.

"I called first, after dinner, and when you didn't answer, I called the desk and asked them to try. They said they'd been trying because the smoke alarm button was flashing for my co-op, but they couldn't get anyone to answer. I came straight home then."

"I really don't think Enrico would have hurt me," Andrea said. "He was violent and melodramatic but not murderous."

"I don't feel particularly reassured by your faith in him," Race said dryly. "He was holding you over that ledge, looking too much like a genuine maniac for me to believe that."

"Still, he let me go."

"I find . . . his gallantry at that point a bit hard to admire."

"He was."

"Believe what you will," Race said, shrugging indifferently. "One thing I've learned about you is that you stubbornly love to believe the most irrational things."

"I do not."

"Next thing you'll be saying is that he saved you from me."

"No. I would never say that," Andrea said softly.

"I should have known that you wouldn't have the ordinary sullen ex, but a wildly crazy one that would sock me right in my broken ribcage the minute he met me."

"You can't blame me for that."

Race chuckled at the sound in her voice of her rising temper. "You married him, didn't you?"

"I suppose I did," she admitted weakly.

"You were like an investment he was determined to cash in on."

"But he did. You can't imagine how much money of mine he's run through."

"Why did you put up with him?"

"I felt sorry for him. I kept thinking I could help him."

"No wonder he was so determined to get you back."

"He just wanted to use me right from the beginning."

"It must be your red hair." His fingers moved caressingly through the tumbling masses of the silken flames. "I never really knew a redhead well before. Tell me, do they all get into as much trouble as you?"

"Perhaps since you're so interested in the subject, you should conduct a study."

"Perhaps I should. But there's only one redhead I want to study in depth," he returned huskily. His hand moved over her breasts to her belly, where he let it linger. His fingers traced the gentle mound lovingly, toying with her navel. "Don't you think it's time to tell me, Andrea," Race spoke softly against her earlobe, in a voice that was undeniably intense.

She shifted nervously. "Tell you what?" she mumbled defensively.

"About the baby."

"About . . ." She sat bolt upright, her body sliding against his. "Oh Race, you devil. How long have you known—without telling me?"

"Ever since I came to New York."

"And you didn't tell me," she gasped.

"*You* didn't tell *me.*"

"I couldn't," she said at last. "Because . . ."

"Apparently there's a lot we didn't tell each other," he said with a chuckle. "You know we're going to have to do something about that. If we're to make a success of our marriage. They say that failure to communicate is one of the most common reasons for divorce. And the last thing I'd say you need is another crazy ex. And I'd be as crazy as Enrico if you left me and we divorced."

"Race, is this mixed-up bunch of verbiage a proposal?"

"No."

"What?" Her pale face went blank with disappointment.

"I'm waiting for you to ask me first," he said smiling. "After all, you're to blame for this whole mess and that I'm an unwed father! You seduced me first that last night on *The Jordana.*"

Catching his mood, she drew a swift breath and smiled saucily. "Last I heard it takes two to tango, my darling, and I think I'll ask you for the next dance."

He rolled his body on top of hers in bold acceptance.

"And maybe later I'll ask you to marry me," she said.

"The answer's yes," he said with a smile, "with a honeymoon in Peru so you can explore Machu Picchu to your heart's content."

"You do know all the weaknesses in my flawed character," she replied.

"I hope not all. I was hoping to discover a few more. Since some of them are so very delightful." There was an erotic element in his deep voice that made her go hot and shivery with excitement. "So when do we get married?" he whispered.

"I haven't asked you—yet," she murmured, "but I might just do the asking . . . if you'll break the bad news to Luci."

"It's a deal."

"That may not be so easy, my darling."

"Why not?"

"It's obvious you haven't met Luci."

"Oh, Lord, I don't like that mischievous twinkle in your eyes. Don't tell me your agent is as crazy as your ex."

"Not now . . . but after you tell her I'm quitting, I don't want to be around. She can be so . . . so . . ."

"So . . . what?"

"So volcanic when it comes to money."

He drew a deep breath in mock resignation. "I always knew—it wasn't going to be easy—being married to you," he said, deliberately suppressing a smile. "It's obvious you're determined to assign me all the hard jobs."

"What's a man for, my darling?"

Her question was deliberately provocative. He was aware of the lightness of her fingertips against his skin as she smoothed his black hair against his temple.

"That's what I'm going to show you—right now," he murmured huskily as his hot lips closed over hers.

Silhouette Sensation

COMING NEXT MONTH

TIMES CHANGE
Nora Roberts

If you read TIME WAS, you'll enjoy meeting Caleb
Hornblower's brother Jacob, who is determined to
find his sibling and take him back where he
belongs—the future!

But when Jacob reaches the cabin he finds only
Sunny Stone, a very enlightened female, but not
someone who would immediately guess that the man
she was falling in love with was a space voyager
from another time!

WITHOUT WARNING
Ann Williams

For ten agonizing years, Blair Mallory mourned
Michael Baldwin's tragic death, grieving for the love
that had died with him.

Now, Michael had mysteriously stepped back into
her life, six feet of flesh and blood, very much alive.
With his dark eyes shining with revenge and remorse,
he asked for her help...

Silhouette Sensation

COMING NEXT MONTH

MAYBE THIS TIME
Dee Holmes

Widowed Elizabeth Healy and her baby daughter needed to be taken to safety and Zach Stone knew where his duty lay. But when a blizzard trapped them at an inn together, Zach realized just what he had been missing…

Elizabeth discovered that beneath his rough, street-smart cop's exterior lurked a tender heart. So why did he try to make loving him impossible?

MORNING STAR
Kristin James

Cathleen Richards was being torn in two; why was she so drawn to the man she blamed for her father's dwindling career?

C.J. Casey saw that Cathleen could have it all—fame, fortune, success; would she throw it all away out of a misguided sense of loyalty? Could she forget the past?

COMING NEXT MONTH FROM

Silhouette

FOR BETTER
FOR WORSE

An unforgettable story of broken dreams and new beginnings

Penny Jordan is set to take the bestseller lists by storm again this autumn, with her stunning new novel which is a masterpiece of raw emotion.

A story of obsessions...
A story of choices...
A story of love.

LARGE-FORMAT
PAPERBACK AVAILABLE
FROM NOVEMBER

PRICED: £8.99

WORLDWIDE

TAKE 4 NEW SILHOUETTE SENSATIONS FREE!

Silhouette Sensations are thrilling romances for today's woman. A specially selected range of romantic fiction seasoned with suspense. You'll also find glamour, sensuality and daring in each thoroughly modern tale.

We're so sure that you'll enjoy your FREE Sensations that we've another treat in store! You could go on to have 4 Silhouette Sensations delivered to your door every month for only £1.85 each (we pay for postage and packing!).

No strings attached - you may cancel or suspend your subscription at any time.

EXTRA FREE GIFT
If you reply within 10 days
Post the Coupon below NOW and we'll send you this cuddly teddy PLUS a mystery gift!

--- ✂ -----

To: Silhouette Reader Service, FREEPOST,
PO Box 236, Croydon, Surrey CR9 9EL

NO STAMP NEEDED

Please rush me 4 Silhouette Sensations and 2 FREE gifts! Please also reserve me a Reader Service subscription, which means I can look forward to receiving 4 brand new Sensations for only £7.40 each month, postage and packing FREE. If I choose not to subscribe, I shall write to you within 10 days and still keep my FREE books and gifts. I may cancel or suspend my subscription at any time. I am over 18 years. Please write in BLOCK CAPITALS.

Ms/Mrs/Miss/Mr _____ EP46SS

Address _____

_____

_____ Postcode _____

Signature _____